D0607032

2250

CONTRACT INTERIOR FINISHES

CONTRACT

INTERIOR

FINISHES

A HANDBOOK OF MATERIALS,

PRODUCTS, AND APPLICATIONS

WILLIAM R. HALL

WHITNEY LIBRARY OF DESIGN

AN IMPRINT OF WATSON-GUPTILL PUBLICATIONS/NEW YORK

The images on pages 218–219 appear courtesy of
Wood Moulding & Millwork Producers Association,
P.O. Box 25278, Portland, Oregon 97225,
(503) 292-9288.

The material on pages 228–234 appears courtesy of
MASTERSPEC® Specifications System,
a product of the Professional Systems Division of
The American Institute of Architects,
1735 New York Avenue N.W., Washington, D.C. 20606,
(800) 424-5080.

Published in 1993 in the United States
by Whitney Library of Design,
an imprint of Watson-Guptill Publications,
a division of BPI Communications, Inc.,
1515 Broadway, New York, NY 10036

Library of Congress Cataloging-in-Publication Data

Hall, William R.
    Contract interior finishes: a handbook of materials, products,
and applications / William R. Hall.
      p.   cm.
    Includes index.
    ISBN 0-8320-0933-5
    1. Building—Details. 2. Commercial buildings—Design and
construction. 3. Finishes and finishing. I. Title.
TH2025.H33 1993
747'.852—dc20   93-2499
                                             CIP

Copyright © 1993 by William R. Hall

All rights reserved. No part of this publication may be
reproduced or used in any form or by any means—graphic,
electronic, or mechanical, including photocopying, recording,
taping, or information storage and retrieval systems—without
written permission of the publisher.

Manufactured in the United States of America

First printing, 1993

1 2 3 4 5 6 7 8 9 / 01 00 99 98 97 96 95 94 93

TO MY WIFE, PHYLLIS,

AND MY CHILDREN JULIANNE, CHRIS, AND ROBBIE,

WITHOUT WHOSE PATIENCE AND SUPPORT

THIS BOOK WOULD NOT HAVE BEEN WRITTEN

CONTENTS

PREFACE

When I began my career in interior design in the early to mid-1970s, I often witnessed a disparity between the concerns and goals of my colleagues and those of the architects with whom they worked. Many interior designers simply didn't bother to consider the structural or aesthetic intent of an architect's design within their own work, and a vast majority of architects trivialized interior design, viewing it contemptuously as the domain of "decorators"—those who simply picked finishes.

Later, while pursuing a master of architecture degree and throughout my professional internship, I gained insight into this problem and thought seriously about what could be done to alleviate it. As a result of countless conversations with the representatives of a wide variety of finish materials manufacturers, I realized that a common thread within client complaints was dissatisfaction with a finish's performance, which was intertwined with its suitability within the context of a particular site. In the majority of cases, the problem could have been avoided if the designer (or the architect, for that matter) had conducted adequate research, focusing in particular on the manufacturer's guidelines and restrictions for installation and maintenance.

After consulting with the dean of the interior design department where I received my bachelor of arts degree and completing some preliminary research, I decided to write a book about the contract, or commercial, end of the profession. In view of what I had experienced, and stirred by my career's conflicting spheres of influence, I felt that a technical treatment of the research, specification, and scheduling of interior finishes for the interior designer was sorely needed. Not coincidentally, this was reflected by a growing trend within interior design education toward more specific technical training.

Claims of humility aside, it must be said that this book is not an exhaustive encyclopedia of every interior finish available to the profession; this would be both impossible and undesirable, as new finishes, products, and materials—and imaginative ways of using them—are continually being developed. Rather, this book, which is a collection of information from a wide range of sources, is intended to cover the major categories of finishes in enough depth to stimulate and broaden the designer's thinking as he or she develops a project's specifications. If they are armed with a thorough understanding of the basic properties and applications of each finish, designers can then be free to use finishes in novel and innovative ways. If the designer requires further information, he or she will know which questions to ask, and where (or from whom) the answers may be obtained.

This book is also intended for interior design students who would like to acquire a solid grounding in the fundamentals of finish specification. Because their primary area of expertise is the specifics of building components, architects who wish to supplement their approach to finishes with an interior designer's point of view will also find it useful.

I would like to extend my gratitude and offer thanks to those who so generously contributed and granted permission to use their photographic materials: the representatives of professional organizations and manufacturers and the private individuals who spent considerable time and effort helping me learn about what is discussed herein. I would also like to thank my employers, whose patience throughout this project's research, development, and writing was greatly appreciated.

INTRODUCTION

Over the course of a career, most contract interior designers encounter a wide variety of projects, an extremely diverse set of products, and a tremendously varied clientele. In the past, most designers were expected to educate themselves primarily about the various materials they used, as well as how they could be grouped to make pleasing combinations.

Today's client is generally more demanding of the interior design profession, and has come to expect knowledge and expertise in such finish-related areas as wearability, lightfastness, and suitability, as well as pricing. As a result of this and other modifying influences, the profession is evolving from merely choosing finishes and "putting together" a space (in some ways a broad generalization) to researching preliminary choices for interior finishes to ensure that they comply with the needs of the project, specifying these products in written form, and following through in a professional manner with the supervision of their installation. In addition, the profession is also concerned with whether finishes will perform adequately over time within the budget allowed.

GENERAL PROCEDURES

Though a wide range of finishes will be discussed in the chapters that follow, there are several topics common to each that are covered consistently throughout the book. However, because every topic cannot be covered in every chapter in the same depth, the designer should keep a few general areas in mind when evaluating and choosing all finish materials or products.

FIRE RATINGS

Because the codes vary among municipalities, fire ratings are not covered in depth. However, since designers must occasionally deal with fire ratings, it is an area about which they should at least be generally aware.

It may be difficult to comprehend, but it is the simple truth that some builders and finish manufacturers would prefer not to spend money to make their buildings or products safe from fire. As a result, local legislators and building officials have found it necessary to institute and enforce fire ratings regulations. These regulations are divided into two general areas: one relates to finish materials themselves, the other relates to the building system. Both areas are connected with the fire requirements that are covered in the local building codes.

In regard to finishes, several rating system categories have been established to classify materials with respect to their ability or inability to resist fire, the speed with which they burn, and the amount of smoke that they generate. If there are general requirements for a particular material, it can usually be assumed that its manufacturers have already incorporated them into their products.

In the chapters that follow, areas of special concern are covered when necessary. If the fire rating requirements of a finish are not discussed, the reader can safely assume that the restrictions are either obvious or would be immediately evident. For instance, stone and ceramic tile are inherently fire resistant, so no requirements are necessary. Untreated wood paneling, on the other hand, has no fire resistance at all; therefore, care should be taken as to where it is installed.

The placement of products relates to another area of fire resistance: the building system. The placement and construction of a building's dividing elements are governed by the building code and regulated to enable all occupants to exit from the building safely in the event of a fire. This is done by requiring that certain corridors and rooms meet specific fire rating requirements. The designer must then determine if there are any restrictions that apply to a finish material within a particular space. For example, certain wallcoverings cannot be used in fire-rated corridors, and many codes prohibit carpeting in stairwells, especially those that connect several floors.

Without an extensive discussion of fire codes and fire resistance, it is impossible to give advice that covers every situation. It is recommended that, when a question arises, designers consult with their local building officials. They will provide the information necessary to make appropriate choices when selecting and placing finishes.

MEASURING AND ORDERING

Each type or category of finish has a standard unit of measurement that is associated with it, and in which manufacturers expect to receive their orders: Carpeting is sold by the square yard, tile by the square foot, molding by the linear foot, and so on. The designer should be aware of the unit of measurement appropriate for each finish so that the budget can be properly tabulated.

The designer must also carefully consider a manufacturer's ordering and delivery restrictions. For instance, delivery for an order of furniture may take 60 to 120 days, possibly more in some cases. On the other hand, particular patterns or materials may be stocked for a quick delivery or specifically made for a project upon receipt of the order. The designer must take these variables into account in order to keep the project on schedule and, most important, to keep the client happy. Nothing is more damaging to a designer's reputation than to tell the client that something will be delivered in one week when in fact it will take three.

CARE AND MAINTENANCE

In some respects, the care and maintenance of interior finishes are matters of common sense. Following the installation of any finish, a care and maintenance program should be instituted to preserve and maintain it. Although the subjects of care and maintenance are covered for the specific category of finish in most of the chapters that follow, there are a few basic principles that designers should always keep in mind.

Dust and grit should be considered the mortal enemies of most finishes, especially flooring surfaces. These microscopic particles have sharp edges that can slowly destroy the surface of the finish. If they are regularly removed, the longevity of a finish can be extended significantly.

Even with regular dusting or sweeping, periodic cleanings are also recommended. In many cases, the manufacturer will suggest a mild soap and water or specially formulated cleaning solution to remove the dirt and grime that light cleanings leave behind. Rather than being forced to do major cleaning infrequently, it is much easier—and better for the finish—to clean lightly or moderately on a regular basis.

Finally, specifying the appropriate material for the particular location or use ensures that a finish will perform as intended for many years. If a designer knowingly specifies a "light-duty" finish in an area that will receive heavy traffic or use, he or she should make the client aware of this fact and outline a vigilant maintenance program to help prolong its life.

1

INTERIOR SUBSTRUCTURES: FLOORS, WALLS, AND CEILINGS

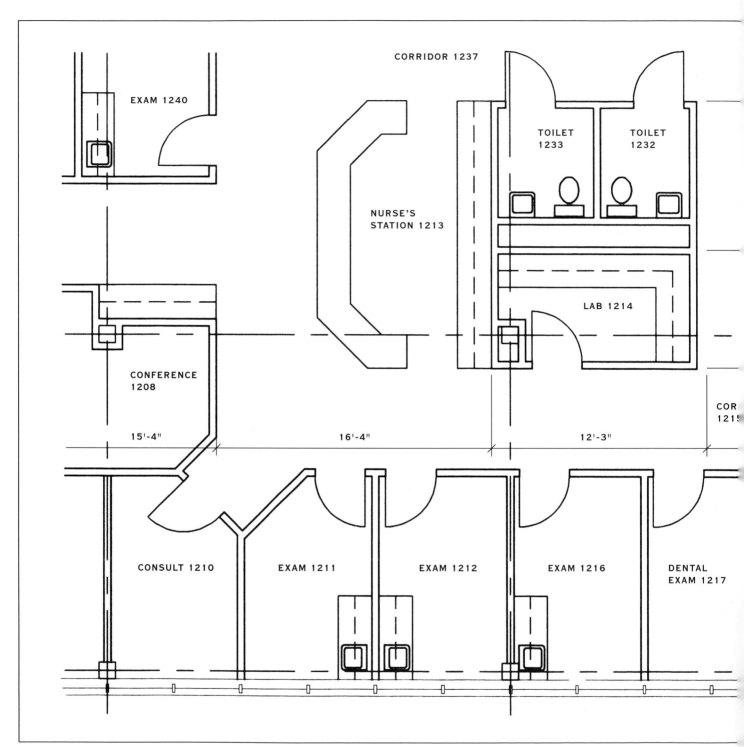

EXAM 1240

CORRIDOR 1237

TOILET 1233

TOILET 1232

NURSE'S STATION 1213

LAB 1214

CONFERENCE 1208

COR 1215

15'-4"

16'-4"

12'-3"

CONSULT 1210

EXAM 1211

EXAM 1212

EXAM 1216

DENTAL EXAM 1217

AN ARCHITECTURAL PLAN OF A HOSPITAL FLOOR SHOWING THE BASIC DIVISIONS OF THE SPACE.

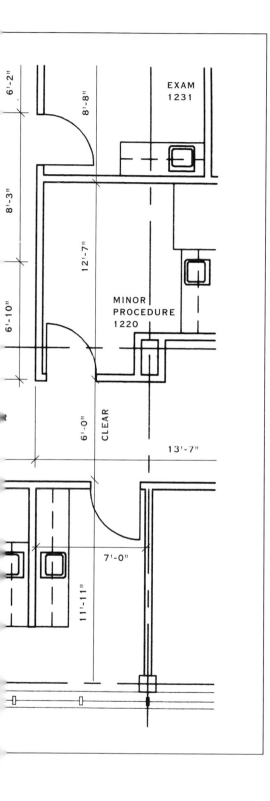

In most instances, interior finishes are designed to be applied to preexisting surfaces. These surfaces—the majority of which are integrally related to architectural structures—support and stabilize finish materials so that they can function and look as the designer intends. However, these underlying structures also fulfill less superficial, more basic objectives: As intrinsic components of the buildings of which they are a part, they provide structural support, conceal structural elements, or divide interior space.

In most examples of contract or commercial interior design, finishes are installed upon or applied to existing or previously constructed interior surfaces. Regardless of the scope of the job, the designer should know which substrate elements are involved so that he or she can serve the client more effectively. Even if the designer only selects finishes and oversees their installation, he or she should be aware of the many types of subsurfaces that might be encountered and how each influences the choice of finish materials. This is particularly important for projects that require interior space planning—including such services as moving or building interior walls and coordinating the locations of doors, interior glazing, phones, electrical outlets, and other related elements—especially since client requests for such services are becoming increasingly common.

For these reasons, we need first to discuss substrates and how they affect finishes. We will also discuss special substrates and structures, as well as related elements that are generally, but not necessarily, more decorative in nature.

The floor is the part of the architecture that receives the most wear and is subject to the most abuse. Because of this, the designer should ask the client about the type of wear each general area of the floor will receive to determine whether the surfaces chosen will be appropriate, and whether or not the subfloor will properly support the flooring specified. A designer's main concern is not necessarily the type and strength of the subfloor, but whether it will adequately support the desired flooring material in an appropriate manner.

WOOD SUBFLOORS

With few exceptions, a *subfloor*, or flooring substrate, is made from either a wood or a cementitious material. A wood subfloor is normally supported from below by a series of *joists*, which are horizontal lengths of wood that transfer the *load*, or weight, of the floor and everything that stands on it to the supporting columns or walls. (A concrete subfloor transfers this load by buttressing the floor itself with steel-reinforcing rods as well as concrete or steel joists.)

For instance, in an older building whose floor substrate is wood, a designer should investigate whether a rigid flooring surface such as tile or brick would be problematic. Because wood is flexible—it expands and contracts in response to heat and cold—its movement might crack the grout or loosen the tiles or bricks. However, if rigid flooring is desired in such a case, there are special materials such as epoxy mortars or setting beds that help to stiffen the entire floor surface. Wood subfloors are most commonly made from plywood, wafer board, or other similar materials. The composition of these materials is discussed in Chapter 2, "Wood."

CONCRETE SUBFLOORS

Cementitious substrates—for walls as well as for floors—are much more common in contemporary structures designed for commercial use than any other material. One type of cementitious subfloor is a simple concrete slab, usually about 4 inches thick, that either serves as the floor to the basement story or as the main floor of a building without a basement. The slab is placed directly on the ground, referred to as a *slab on grade*, which provides support to keep it in place.

There are a few potential problems that a designer should keep in mind when specifying flooring material for a concrete slab. Moisture that naturally migrates through the slab will hinder the adhesion of most flooring surfaces. Small hairline cracks are reasonably common and not usually problematic; however, larger, more open cracks can be troublesome. If a crack continues to spread, or if one side of the crack is not level with the other, the crack will "telegraph" through the finish and crack or distort the flooring surface, thus damaging its installation. There are some products that are made to fill small to medium-sized cracks (Florestone, for example), but they will not prevent a crack from spreading. Obviously, these considerations will affect—and perhaps even change—a designer's choice of finish, once research is done to see if these kinds of problems can be dealt with if they are present in the project.

Another form of concrete subfloor is part of a system of corrugated steel deck laid across steel joists. The concrete, which can either be standard concrete or one incorporating a lightweight aggregate, is poured over the deck to a thickness of about 3 inches. This creates a monolithic, noncombustible surface that yields a strong floor with minimal deflection. Almost any finish would be suitable with this type of subfloor.

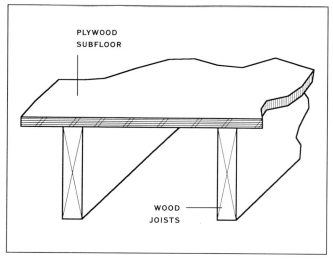

A CROSS SECTION OF A WOOD FLOOR AND ITS UNDERLYING STRUCTURE.

PLYWOOD SUBFLOOR

WOOD JOISTS

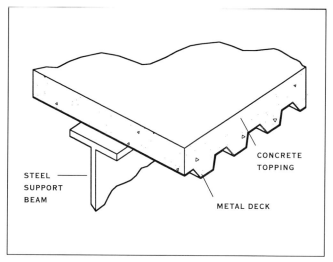

A CROSS SECTION OF A CONCRETE FLOOR AND ITS STEEL SUPPORT STRUCTURE.

STEEL SUPPORT BEAM

CONCRETE TOPPING

METAL DECK

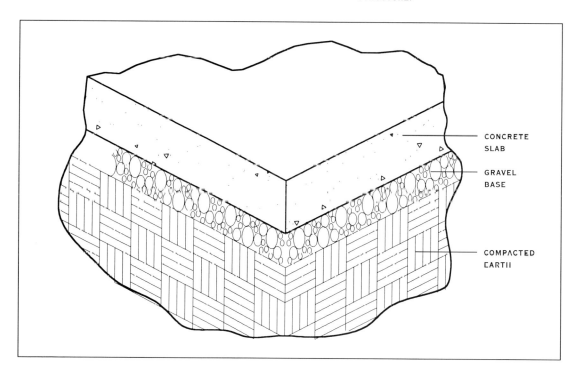

A CROSS SECTION OF A CONCRETE SLAB ON GRADE.

CONCRETE SLAB

GRAVEL BASE

COMPACTED EARTH

A CROSS SECTION OF A WOOD SUBFLOOR SUPPORTING A LIGHTWEIGHT CONCRETE TOPPING. A COMMON CONSTRUCTION METHOD IN RESIDENTIAL APARTMENTS AND WOOD-FRAMED COMMERCIAL BUILDINGS, THIS CONFIGURATION GIVES THE FLOOR A MORE SOLID FEEL.

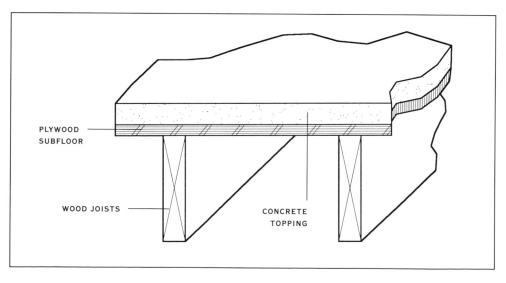

PLYWOOD SUBFLOOR

WOOD JOISTS

CONCRETE TOPPING

WALLS

Walls also provide a background or support surface for interior finishes. Walls can perform as both exterior and interior elements and may or may not be a part of the structure. Although there are a wide variety of wall construction types, for the purposes of this discussion we will divide them into two main categories: those walls whose finishes reflect their materials of construction, and those whose surfaces require further finish.

In the first category, brick, stone, and concrete are all examples of walls that normally require no final finish because the composition of the wall *is* the finish. These walls are usually constructed when the building itself is built, and are chosen when the material of the wall will not be used as a base for another finish. (Information regarding specific finishes can be found in the following chapters.) The second category is comprised of walls that will serve as a subsurface for a final finish. Finishes that require some sort of undersupport for proper application include paint, wallcovering, tile, and paneling.

There is some overlap between these categories. For instance, one may wish to paint or tile over an existing brick wall or install wood paneling over concrete block. On the other hand, an existing finish may be removed to expose the material of the wall beneath. In spite of these occasional alternatives, the two categories described above reflect the most common circumstances that a designer will encounter; in addition, the second category encompasses, by far, the vast majority of situations. There are two basic types of wall substrates that normally provide a base for other finishes: plaster and drywall.

PLASTER

One of the oldest forms of wall finish material, plaster covers an existing surface with a pasty substance which then hardens to a smooth, flat surface that conceals the one underneath. While the first material used as plaster was probably mud, Greek and then Roman builders developed various successful plaster mixes that dried smooth and flat. These early plasters merely required a subsurface with a *tooth*, or texture (usually a rock or rubble masonry wall), providing a base on which the material could be applied and to which it could easily adhere. Through the centuries that followed, plaster became the primary method for creating the interior wall surfaces upon which a wide variety of final finish materials were applied.

Until the process of manufacturing drywall was perfected in the 1950s, plaster was the predominant method of creating an even, flat interior surface, both commercially and residentially, and was also used to make highly detailed ornamental forms. Although plaster and drywall contain the same basic ingredient, gypsum, plaster's surface is harder and more dense, making it more prone to cracks and less tolerant of movement, and its installation requires costly skilled labor. As a result of these drawbacks, plaster was all but replaced following the introduction of drywall, which is sold in standard-sized sheets that can be installed more quickly and easily than a plaster wall.

Recently, however, plaster has made a modest comeback. Today it is used to create coved or irregularly shaped surfaces or edges that are impossible to attain with a flat panel. Because it was commonly used as a substrate in projects built before the 1950s, designers should have a general understanding of plaster's composition and installation.

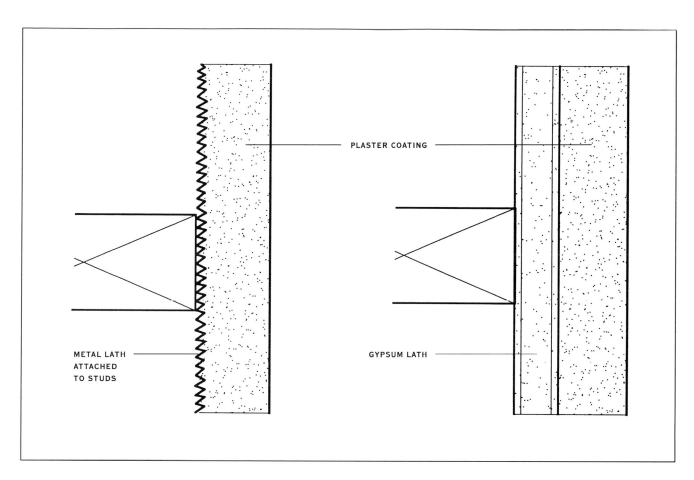

PLASTER COATING

METAL LATH
ATTACHED
TO STUDS

GYPSUM LATH

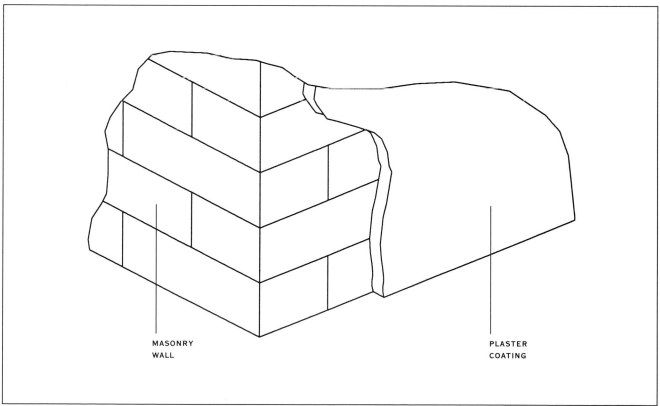

MASONRY
WALL

PLASTER
COATING

PLASTER CAN BE APPLIED TO THREE TYPES OF SUBSTRUCTURES: A METAL LATH *(TOP LEFT)*, A GYPSUM LATH *(TOP RIGHT)*, AND A MASONRY WALL *(BOTTOM)*.

Plaster must be applied to a basic wall structure, which either exists as part of a building or must be constructed. The latter is commonly done with metal or wood studs installed at 16 or 24 inches on center. Next, the *lath*, or the material to which the plaster adheres, is attached to the studs. In buildings constructed prior to the late 1940s, lath consisted of long, thin strips of wood that were attached to the studs horizontally about $1/2$ inch apart, which allowed the plaster to squeeze between the strips to create a bond. Plaster was also applied directly to the interior surface of masonry walls. Today, lath is made of metal mesh or rough gypsum panels that are attached directly to the studs. Metal lath was first used to increase fire resistance, and the use of drywall as lath eventually led to its adoption as a wall surface and the near displacement of plaster. In addition, both materials are more economical and easier to install than wood lath. (A masonry base for plaster is also sometimes still used.) Regardless of its configuration, the lath must be sufficiently rough or open to enable the plaster to bond to the surface beneath.

After the lath has been installed, the first coat, or *scratch coat*, of plaster is applied. The scratch coat is usually composed of a gypsum-based mixture combined with some type of aggregate. (Gypsum plaster without aggregates is known as *neat plaster*, which is specifically made for those who prefer to add aggregate on the job.) These aggregates, which may include wood fibers, mineral-based materials such as sand and perlite, or other similar types of materials, help stabilize the mixture and increase coverage. Each type of aggregate has its own advantages and disadvantages. Designers should consult an experienced plasterer or the local dealer of plaster products for more specific information.

The scratch coat is generally troweled onto and pressed partially through the lath to help produce a strong bond, and then *rodded*, or scratched, with a stiff metal rod to level the surface in preparation for the next coat. In the *lay-on method*, the thickness of the scratch coat is slightly less than that of the finished surface; then only a finish coat is added. In the *double-back method*, the scratch coat is applied in a thin layer. Before it dries, a second coat, called the *hair coat* or *brown coat*, is applied and rodded to a level surface just below the *screeds*, which are strips of wood that are attached to the wall and used as guides to the thickness of each coat. The brown coat is similar in composition to the scratch coat, and is primarily used to fill out the thickness of the surface so that the finish coat can be applied properly. In the *three-coat method*, the scratch coat is thinly applied and pressed into the lath, then raked or scratched with a wire brush to create a rough surface that will enable subsequent coats to bond adequately.

After the scratch coat has been applied (and the brown coat, if used), the final step is the *finish coat*. This is one of the most important steps in the process because it forms the surface on which paint, wallcovering, or other finish materials will be applied. Finish plaster is a mixture of plaster, lime, and water. The proportions of the mixture and the content of each part may vary, modifying the final characteristics of the surface to some degree, but the basic plaster finish is hard and very smooth. The finish coat is applied in much the same way as the other coats: It is troweled onto the surface with a metal trowel and smoothed out level with the screeds. It is a reasonably thin coat that bonds to the brown coat, creating the smooth, hard surface that is normally desired. Since it is applied while in a plastic state, almost any texture or finish is possible. To create a textured surface, the finish coat is applied with wooden or rubber trowels.

A WORKER APPLIES THE SCRATCH COAT OF PLASTER TO A PREPARED GYPSUM LATH. *UNITED STATES GYPSUM COMPANY/USG INTERIORS, INC.*

ONCE THE SCRATCH COAT HAS BEEN RODDED, THE HAIR OR BROWN COAT IS APPLIED. *UNITED STATES GYPSUM COMPANY/USG INTERIORS, INC.*

THE FINISH COAT, A MIXTURE OF PLASTER, LIME, AND WATER, IS THE FINAL STEP IN APPLYING PLASTER. *HARR, HEDRICH-BLESSING; UNITED STATES GYPSUM COMPANY/USG INTERIORS, INC.*

DRYWALL

In homes and buildings constructed after 1950, the most common wall surface is gypsum drywall (also called *gypsum board, plasterboard,* or *Sheetrock).* This surface is manufactured into thin sheets with a gypsum core or body and a heavy paper surface. A tough gray liner paper applied to the back of the panel protects it and gives it some stability. A smooth buff-colored paper covers the front and edges of the panel, and is the surface on which the final finish is applied. Drywall is manufactured in standard 4-foot widths, and lengths of 8, 9, 10, 12, and 14 feet. The most common thicknesses are $1/2$ inch and $5/8$ inch. (Less common but still standard are $1/4$-inch and $3/8$-inch thicknesses; 1-inch-thick utility panels are also available.)

Because it is economical and relatively simple to install, drywall has become so popular that it has virtually replaced plaster as a wall surface. The final result is suitable for painting, or as a base for wallcovering, texturing, tile, and a variety of other finishes.

DRYWALL IN CONSTRUCTION

Drywall is normally installed on wood or metal studs and attached with special nails or screws. Because the surface of a wall constructed with drywall is comprised of a number of individual panels whose edges meet in butt joints, the joints must be joined or covered to create a monolithic wall surface. These joints are the weak points in walls constructed of drywall. When cracks or problems occur, they are most commonly found at the joints. Therefore, correctly installed drywall includes properly finished joints.

The method of finishing drywall consists of spreading each joint with joint compound or *mud,* which is a paste made of powdered gypsum and water, and then covering it with strips of 2- to 3-inch-wide paper tape. The drywall installer applies the mud to the joint, smooths it level with the adjacent wall surfaces, then presses the tape into the soft joint. A bit more mud is smoothed over the tape, creating a joint that is about 6 inches wide. After the base coat has dried and been sanded, second and third coats of a material known as *topping compound* are applied in the same manner. This material is softer and dries faster than joint compound, allowing the imperfections to be sanded out more easily. These coats are applied in wider 9- and 12-inch coats respectively, and are sanded after they have dried. Therefore, when the joint is finished, there is a wide, tapered area that covers the joint well and appears smooth with the surrounding wall surfaces.

Inside corners are prepared using joint tape that has been folded at a 90-degree angle. In a manner similar to the preparation of standard joints, it is covered with mud and pressed into the corner, smoothed with a special corner tool, then finished as described above.

Since outside corners are subject to more abuse than the inside corners and flat parts of a wall, a thin, metal angle or *corner bead* is nailed over the corner before the mud is applied in a manner similar to that described above. After the joint dries it is sanded down; then two more coats are added and sanded.

Nails and screws that are not located along a joint are not taped. Instead, a series of coats of mud are applied over each head. Each coat is sanded so that it will blend in with the surrounding area. When the third coat is sanded, special attention is given to any area that might not be smooth enough. If a textured surface is desired, drywall mud can be applied at this point in a variety of ways. In general, after the third coat of topping compound has been sanded, it is ready for the final finish, whatever it might be.

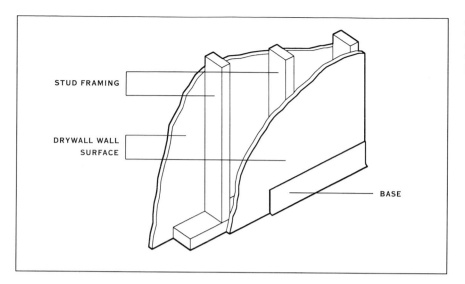

A CROSS SECTION
OF A WALL
CONSTRUCTED OF
WOOD STUDS AND
DRYWALL.

STUD FRAMING

DRYWALL WALL
SURFACE

BASE

THE PROGRESSIVE
LAYERS OF A
DRYWALL JOINT.

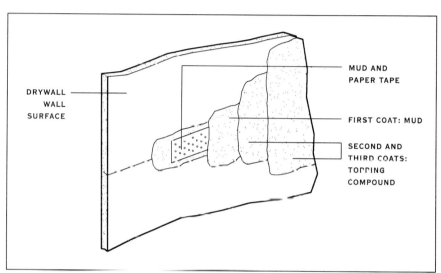

DRYWALL
WALL
SURFACE

MUD AND
PAPER TAPE

FIRST COAT: MUD

SECOND AND
THIRD COATS:
TOPPING
COMPOUND

DRYWALL CORNERS:
INSIDE AND OUTSIDE.

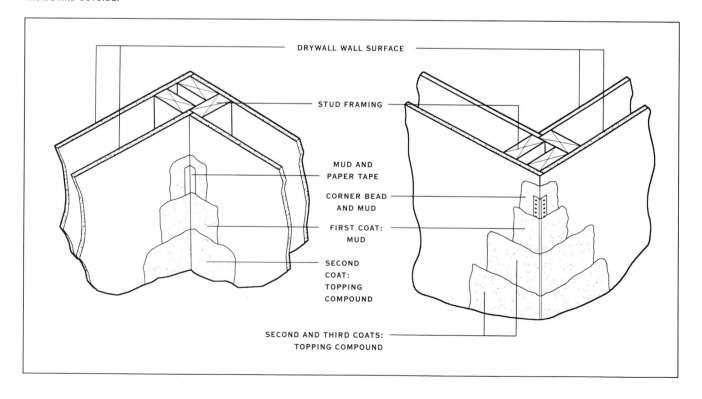

DRYWALL WALL SURFACE

STUD FRAMING

MUD AND
PAPER TAPE

CORNER BEAD
AND MUD

FIRST COAT:
MUD

SECOND
COAT:
TOPPING
COMPOUND

SECOND AND THIRD COATS:
TOPPING COMPOUND

SPECIAL TYPES OF DRYWALL

There are a few special varieties of drywall that a designer should be familiar with. For use in areas of high moisture, such as restrooms or sink areas in kitchens, a water-resistant gypsum board or *green board*—so named after the greenish color of its surface paper—is produced. Note that this board is not water*proof;* it only resists the penetration of water that may occur in damp areas.

Because of the water contained in gypsum's molecular structure, all drywall is inherently fire-resistant. A special type, *type X gypsum board*—which is stamped "type X" or "FR" on the back for identification—is reinforced with fiberglass and contains fire-retardant additives. When used with 2 × 4 inch wood or 3⅝-inch metal studs, the assembly automatically yields an approved fire rating.

Predecorated drywall is standard gypsum board with a factory-applied vinyl wallcovering on the surface. Requiring a bit more care in installation, the standard drywall jointing procedures have been replaced with vinyl molding or a simple V groove between panels. The wallcovering choices are somewhat limited, but these panels are useful where time is an important factor, as they eliminate the final finish altogether. This type of drywall is normally used in conjunction with standard movable or demountable wall partitions, which are discussed later in this chapter.

SPECIAL USES OF DRYWALL

Because drywall is manufactured in large flat panels, many people consider it primarily as a standard wall surface. With proper backing, however, it can be used in many situations. Functional shapes are very common. For example, light soffits can take a wide variety of configurations, but a drywall soffit can hide the light source, allowing the light to shine from behind. (Perimeter and indirect lighting both use this technique.) The soffit's exact configuration will vary with the lighting requirements and the wishes of the designer.

Another primarily functional use of drywall is as *drywall beams,* which are actually steel, concrete, or wood beams of a building structure that are encased in drywall. In the case of large steel joists, the bottom and angular members may also be enclosed individually, creating architectural shapes that aren't as sterile as painted steel joists might be.

A CROSS SECTION OF A LIGHT COVE CONSTRUCTED OF METAL STUDS AND DRYWALL.

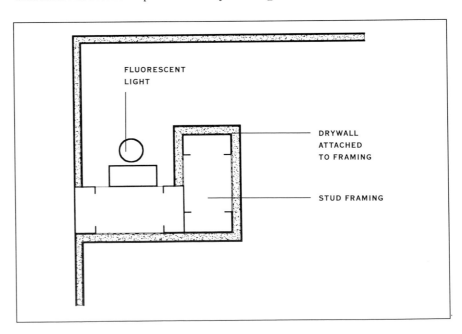

FLUORESCENT LIGHT

DRYWALL ATTACHED TO FRAMING

STUD FRAMING

Drywall is also commonly used for a wide variety of design-oriented shapes. For instance, with an arrangement of steel studs and drywall, one can create a series of perimeter steps between the wall or ceiling. False beams and columns are also possible. The only limitations are the size of the steel studs used to frame the drywall and the way they are put together.

Although it might seem impossible at first, flat drywall panels can be bent around steel studs arranged to create curved walls. This technique requires moistening the front and back of the panels with water and allowing them to set in a stack for an hour, which will help the panels soften and bend more easily. After installation, the drywall will dry to its original hardness.

Installing curved drywall also requires that the studs are positioned closer together than normal. The smaller the radius of the curve, the closer the studs should be placed. A curve with a radius of less than 5 feet is possible but is not recommended, even when using 1/4-inch drywall, as it calls for the installation of many thin strips. With the many joints that this type of curved wall requires, the mudding and sanding process is much more difficult and time-consuming than installing standard drywall walls, but the results are especially pleasing.

The uses of drywall are probably limited only by the designer's knowledge of the material and his or her imagination. With a little research, special uses of drywall can greatly enhance an interior design program. The designer should consult with a drywall installer about special shapes and configurations to ensure that he or she is comfortable with fabricating them.

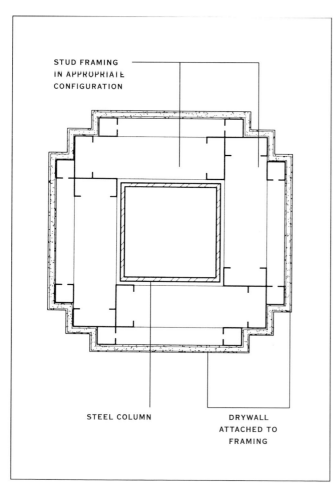

AN OVERHEAD CROSS SECTION OF A COLUMN BUILT OF METAL STUDS AND DRYWALL.

A CURVED STAIRWAY WALL CONSTRUCTED OF DRYWALL DURING (ABOVE) AND AFTER CONSTRUCTION (LEFT).

Predecorated vinyl drywall panels (discussed earlier in this chapter) are primarily used as movable or demountable partitions. These systems can be easily moved or reconfigured to meet new requirements with minimal waste, with approximately 50 to 70 percent of the wall that can be used again. When compared to standard drywall and steel stud construction, where almost nothing is reusable, the savings can be significant. This is highly desirable in interiors that require remodeling regularly, such as with growing businesses and in buildings whose tenants change frequently.

There are two methods used by manufacturers to create this type of wall. Both systems use modular wall panels in 24- or 30-inch increments with special base and ceiling moldings to hide the panel edges. One type uses specially formed H- or T-shaped metal studs with panels that have slotted and beveled vertical edges. The edge slot allows the panels to fit into the edge of the H-stud snugly, holding them in place. The beveled edges create a pleasing joint without having to align the panels perfectly flat. Specially made ceiling and floor tracks tie the assembly together, keeping installation simple.

Another type of demountable wall system uses a series of steel floor and ceiling tracks with a thick inner drywall panel enclosed in two ½-inch-thick panels with beveled vertical edges on each side. The inner panel is offset from the outer panels an inch or so, creating an interconnecting tongue-and-groove system between them.

Both systems can meet standard office electrical requirements for wiring, plugs, and switches. Doors and windows can also be added to each system while still retaining a reasonable degree of movability. However, the designer should keep in mind that, outside of the modularity of the wall system itself, doors, windows, and electrical hardware are installed conventionally in these walls, which, in most cases, creates special sections that can only be used again if the existing configurations will work in the new location.

A CROSS SECTION OF ONE TYPE OF DEMOUNTABLE WALL. *UNITED STATES GYPSUM COMPANY/USG INTERIORS, INC.*

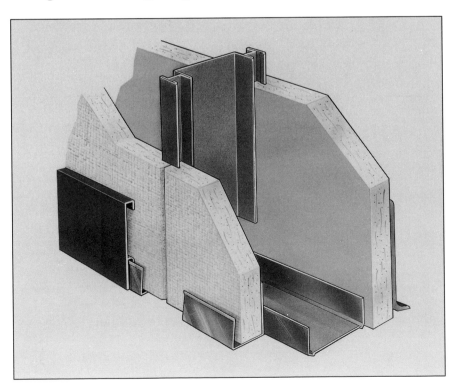

CEILINGS

Ceilings serve much the same purpose as walls: They enclose space and define the interior environment. In most cases, a ceiling consists of the horizontal surface above the walls, and may be composed of exposed concrete, steel, and wood, as well as plaster, drywall, and a number of other materials and products. Ceilings may also enclose or hide the structural, mechanical, and electrical elements of the roof or floor above. They are sometimes used to regulate the acoustics of a space and to encase outlets for heating, ventilation, and air conditioning. But ceilings also have a few unique characteristics.

CEILING SUBSTRATES

Assuming that a building is designed to support its interior structures (floors, walls, and ceilings) as well as specified live loads (people, furniture, equipment, and so forth), a designer normally does not worry much about the weight of the finishes that he or she chooses. A floor, because it is flat, will almost always be able to support carpet, vinyl, and most ceramic tiles. Because its surface is vertical, a wall will support a finish by providing adequate *shearing strength* to the finish's adhesive or fasteners, which means that the adhesive or fasteners attached to the wall will help to keep the finish from sliding down the surface of the wall toward the floor. In the case of a ceiling, however, the substrate and any finish material must be suspended from the structure or material above. Since the force of gravity pulls a ceiling down perpendicular to the structure above it, the adhesive or fasteners must be able to support the entire weight of the finish material. The designer must be aware of the weight of the ceiling finish, as well as how the particular finish will be attached to the structure above it.

Because of these considerations, heavy materials such as brick and stone are almost never used. If such a material is desired, it is used in small or thin pieces to reduce the weight. For example, instead of full bricks, special brick pavers that are manufactured to a thickness of about $1/2$ inch are installed on a ceiling in a manner similar to ceramic tile. In any event, any reasonably heavy material that is intended as a ceiling finish will be accompanied by the manufacturer's specific instructions and limitations, which will indicate the procedures and products required to correctly install it. If a material is not recommended for installation on a ceiling but the designer still wishes to use it, he or she must consult the manufacturer or with an engineer for alternative procedures. This can increase material and installation costs, but if the budget can accommodate it, and it is considered critical to the overall design, it can be done.

CEILING CONSTRUCTION

While the materials used for ceiling substrates and their installation are similar to those used for walls (such as plaster and drywall), their support structure and means of construction are different. When installing these materials as ceilings, they are attached to the structure (which usually consists of wood joists or beams) in one of three ways: directly to the structure; by strips or other hardware that are then attached to the structure; or by wires that are attached to the floor above (for suspended ceilings, which are most common in commercial interiors). The method used depends on the design and the spacing of the horizontal elements above the ceiling. When a room or space requires more than one approach, these methods can be combined.

Let's assume for a moment that there are no special design considerations for a project's ceilings. We would like a flat surface, such as drywall, on which another material will be applied. A quick evaluation will determine the best method of installation.

- *Direct installation.* If the ceiling structure consists of simple wood joists, which are normally spaced between 16 and 24 inches apart, the drywall can be nailed directly to the joists.

- *Semidirect installation.* If the joists are larger members that are spaced farther apart (from 24 to 60 inches, for instance), the installed drywall, if attached directly, will tend to warp because the attachment points are too far apart. For this type of structure, furring strips should be installed. These are normally attached to the joists at right angles from 16 to 24 inches apart. Wood structures require wood furring strips; for steel structures, metal furring channels, or *hat channels*, are wired to the bottom of the joists. The drywall is then attached to these furring strips.

- *Suspended installation.* If the structural elements are spaced even farther apart than 60 inches, or if the bottoms of the joists do not coincide with the desired height of the ceiling, a grid of metal elements can be constructed and suspended from the floor above at the desired height; the drywall is then attached to the bottom of the grid. This system can create a ceiling at any height allowable within the parameters of the building, and leaves room for HVAC equipment, large lighting fixtures, special recessed ceiling designs, and other elements.

Because the entire weight of the ceiling is supported by wires, nails, or screws, there are special code requirements for installation that are intended to ensure that the ceiling remains in place. The designer should consult the applicable local building code: For direct or semidirect installation, it usually only specifies the size and frequency of the nails or screws; for suspended ceilings, the code will specify the size and spacing of the suspension wires, which is normally 4 feet in both directions. There may also be seismic requirements that specify the installation of additional wires at 45-degree angles at points 12 feet apart in each direction. During an earthquake, these wires resist movement in the ceiling to keep it from falling or shaking itself apart. (See also Chapter 10, "Ceiling Materials and Finishes," for a discussion of premanufactured suspended ceilings.)

SPECIAL ELEMENTS

The possibilities for special substrate elements are limited only by the material's configurations, its method of installation, and the designer's imagination. Normally, wall and ceiling substrates are flat surfaces with right-angle corners. Adding radiused corners to the wall and ceiling surfaces, for example, can increase labor costs significantly. In addition, if made exclusively of plaster or drywall mud, radiused corners will be difficult to form and will create surfaces that are more susceptible to damage than standard corners and edges. Several companies manufacture forms—usually made of extruded aluminum or metal—that aid in the creation of this type of recurring configuration, allowing many designs to be accomplished more quickly (and thus more cheaply) than would be possible with a complete custom process. These products provide the designer with another means to make his or her design vision a reality.

A SELECTION OF METAL PRESHAPED REVEALS AND CURVES MADE SPECIFICALLY FOR DRYWALL JOINTS. LONGER EXTRUDED SHAPES ARE AVAILABLE FOR LARGER RELIEF FORMS SUCH AS COLUMNS, BEAMS, AND LINTELS. *PITTCON INDUSTRIES*

REVEALS AND SIMPLE CURVES

One popular wall or ceiling element is the *reveal*. Usually presented in the same material that it serves to enhance, a reveal is a recessed groove that creates shadow lines within the material, making the shadowed groove appear darker and, therefore, more prominent. With the use of premanufactured materials, this subtle element is relatively easy to create. The installer simply attaches the shape to the structural support, affixes the drywall or installs the plaster up to its edge, and finishes the element as one would a corner. Premanufactured reveals or reglets come in a variety of depths and widths, allowing for many different treatments. They may be installed horizontally, vertically, or at any angle parallel to the face of the wall, and can also be mitered without too much difficulty.

Radiused corners and joints provide another way to add a different look to a project or room. These were often used in the 1950s with plaster surfaces; with drywall they are quite difficult to create. By using extruded aluminum shapes made for both inside and outside corners, for either plaster or drywall, and available in a variety of radiuses (from 1/2 to 4 inches), the process is considerably simpler. The shapes are installed in a manner similar to that outlined above for reveals, and yield a surprisingly smooth and natural look. They can be used extensively (at all horizontal and vertical joints) or sparingly (as accents).

RELIEF FORMS

Basic substrates can also be modified by using preformed shapes to achieve different and unique motifs. Coffered ceiling elements, decorative or specially shaped beams or columns, light coves, and lintels are all examples of ornamental motifs for which preformed materials can be utilized. These materials are more expensive than plaster or drywall, but, again, the labor costs for their installation are significantly less than those required to create the shapes individually. Each motif is formed from a mold or reverse template, and is usually made of fiberglass or fiberglass-reinforced gypsum. These shapes are then used to create the required number of elements—the greater the number, the greater the economy. The forms are designed to be integrated into standard plaster or drywall substrates if necessary, and to fit together, one into the next, where repetition is required. Preformed shapes are also usually lighter than their drywall or plaster counterparts. In some situations, the designer may be limited by the amount of weight that can be supported by the ceiling or the configuration as designed. In these cases, a preformed shape may be just what is needed.

2

WOOD

THE IMAGINATIVE AND DRAMATIC USE OF WOOD AS DETAIL CONTRIBUTES TO THE COZY AMBIANCE OF THIS BISTRO-STYLE DELICATESSEN.
MASAO UEDA PHOTOGRAPHY; COURTESY OF DORF ASSOCIATES

Because wood is taken from a living, developing organism, the color, grain pattern, and durability of two pieces of wood from two trees of the same species—or even from different parts of the same tree—will not match exactly. These subtle variations are part of the beauty and allure of wood. Interior designers should also be aware of this multifaceted material's more commonplace characteristics, which contribute significantly to its widespread popularity as a finish. Within the constraints of the material and its methods of installation, wood still gives the interior designer much creative latitude.

Trees are composed of three basic systems: the roots, the trunk or stem, and the crown or leafy portion. The roots gather moisture and nourishment from the soil. The trunk, from which the majority of wood is taken, conducts sustenance from the roots and supports the crown. The outer layers of the trunk form the bark, which acts as a protective sheath. A cross-section of the trunk shows the complexity of the internal structure that gives wood its strength and beauty. The *pith*, or the very center of the trunk, is surrounded by concentric *growth rings*, which reflect the development of the tree. Directly beneath the bark is a very thin layer called the *cambium*, where the growth of the tree occurs. Therefore, the growth rings near the center of the trunk are the oldest; the outer rings are the youngest.

Most trees undergo an annual growth cycle that consists of an interval of growth—which usually occurs in the spring—followed by a dormant period. The growth rings also reflect this cycle: The lighter wood is generated during the growth period; the darker portion of the ring, formed during the dormant period, indicates the end of the growing season. As the temperature drops, the sap thickens and moves more slowly, affecting the color of the ring. The size and thickness of the growth rings can vary, depending on the weather, climate, and whether the optimum conditions for a particular species are present in its habitat. The wood of fast-growing trees (such as pine or fir), which usually have wide growth rings, tends to be somewhat soft. The wood of slow-growing trees (such as oak or walnut), which have thinner growth rings, is dense and hard. In smaller trees, branches, and twigs, the wood of the entire trunk or limb is used to move sap, making it lighter in color and softer in structure; hence the term *sapwood*. As a tree grows and ages, less and less of the trunk is needed for sap movement. As a result of this, the inner cells of the trunk die, creating the darker, denser, more durable wood referred to as *heartwood*.

The vast majority of the wood that is used today is sawn into standard sizes and shapes. Obviously, a tree can be cut into a wide variety of shapes, which in turn can come from many different portions of the tree. By definition, the grain of a piece of wood is not uniform: It is circular around the pith and runs parallel to its length. The look and strength of each piece of wood can vary according to how it is cut from the trunk: Boards that are cut across the growth rings (referred to as *flat-sawn* or *flat-grained)* are less likely to warp that those that are cut from the arc of a trunk that has first been cut into quarters *(quarter-sawn* or *edge-grained)*.

Contrary to what one might expect, the terms *softwood* and *hardwood* do not necessarily refer to a piece of wood's relative softness or hardness; instead, they categorize wood based on the type of tree from which it was cut. Conifers or evergreen trees such as pine, spruce, and fir are typical softwoods. Deciduous trees, which drop their leaves in the fall and usually have a much wider spread to their branches, are classified as hardwoods. Although there are some exceptions, most of the softwoods are in fact softer or less dense than the majority of hardwoods.

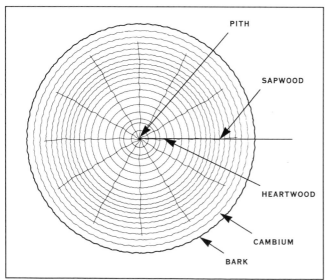

THE CROSS SECTION OF A TREE SHOWS THE ELEMENTS THAT COMPOSE ITS TRUNK: THE PITH, THE HEARTWOOD, THE SAPWOOD, THE CAMBIUM, AND THE BARK.

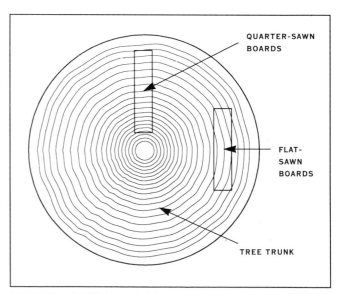

DEPENDING ON HOW A LOG IS CUT—EITHER FLAT SAWN (ACROSS THE GROWTH RINGS) OR QUARTER SAWN (INTO THE RINGS FROM A QUARTERED LOG)—DIFFERENT GRAIN CONFIGURATIONS CAN BE OBTAINED.

LUMBER

Most logs can be cut into pieces of almost any size. A log whose wood is intended to be used in construction is usually cut into a combination of standard sizes, or *lumber,* that best fit its individual size.

In standard terminology, sawn pieces of wood whose smallest dimension is 1 inch or less—1 × 1, 1 × 2, 1 × 4, 1 × 6, and so on—are called *boards,* while the term *dimension lumber* refers to pieces whose smallest dimension is between 1 and 2 inches—2 × 2, 2 × 4, 2 × 6, 2 × 8, and so on. Pieces whose smallest dimension is larger than 2 inches are usually referred to as *timber.*

These standard lumber sizes, which are known as *nominal dimensions,* are the rough sizes of each piece after it is first cut in the mill. These pieces must be planed and smoothed before they are usable, and seasoning and drying further reduce their size. As a result, the actual finished dimensions of a 2 × 4 are 1 1/2 × 3 1/2 inches.

DIMENSION LUMBER SIZES		
	SURFACED DRY	
NOMINAL SIZE (IN INCHES)	NET SIZES (IN INCHES)	AREA (IN SQUARE INCHES)
2 × 3	1 1/2 × 2 1/2	3.75
2 × 4	1 1/2 × 3 1/2	5.25
2 × 6	1 1/2 × 5 1/2	8.25
2 × 8	1 1/2 × 7 1/4	10.87
2 × 10	1 1/2 × 9 1/4	13.87
2 × 12	1 1/2 × 11 1/4	16.87

NOTE: OTHER SIZES ARE AVAILABLE FROM SOME MANUFACTURERS.
SOURCE: *THE WOOD BOOK,* 1992

FINISH LUMBER SIZES			
THICKNESS		WIDTH	
NOMINAL (IN INCHES)	ACTUAL SURFACED DRY (IN INCHES)	NOMINAL (IN INCHES)	ACTUAL SURFACED DRY (IN INCHES)
3/8	5/16	2	1 1/2
1/2	7/16	3	2 1/2
5/8	9/16	4	3 1/2
3/4	5/8	5	4 1/2
1	3/4	6	5 1/2
1 1/4	1	7	6 1/2
1 1/2	1 1/4	8	7 1/4
1 3/4	1 3/8	9	8 1/4
2	1 1/2	10	9 1/4

NOTE: OTHER SIZES ARE AVAILABLE FROM SOME MANUFACTURERS.
SOURCE: *THE WOOD BOOK,* 1992

Plywood consists of a series of *veneers*—very thin slices of wood—that have been glued together to create a flat panel. The term was coined in the early twentieth century, but the material and its general process of application has been used for centuries.

Initially known as *veneering*, the earliest form of plywood was simply a thin layer of one kind of wood glued onto a thicker layer of another kind. Used mostly for decorative purposes, it was applied to art objects and fine furniture from the reign of Tutankhamen through the Greek and Roman periods. After disappearing in Europe during the Middle Ages, veneering reappeared in the late seventeenth and early eighteenth centuries and was used mostly by artisans to embellish exotic furnishings. In the latter half of the nineteenth century, enterprising businessmen realized the potential building applications of laminated wood: its strength, dimensional stability, resistance to warping and splitting, and, during the manufacturing process, its ability to make curved surfaces. Thus, this early art form evolved into one of the most adaptable utilitarian building materials in use today.

MANUFACTURING VENEER

Because plywood is primarily composed of layers of veneer, it is important to understand how wood veneer is made. After the trees are harvested and brought to the mill, the bark is removed by cutting or rubbing it off while the log is spun on a machine similar to a large lathe. The debarked logs are then cut into approximately $8^{1}/_{2}$-foot lengths. These *peeler blocks* are then heated to a uniform temperature so that they can be cut or sliced more easily. There are two primary methods used to cut veneer from a log: peeling and slicing.

The *peeling method* is used to cut most veneers. In this process, the peeler block is placed into a huge lathe, then spun against a full-length knife that peels the veneer away from the log in one long continuous piece. The rate of the lathe's speed depends on many factors, including the species of wood and the thickness of the veneer, which can range from $^{1}/_{10}$ inch to $^{1}/_{4}$ inch. (Hardwoods can be cut to as little as $^{1}/_{200}$ inch.) The 3- to 4-inch spindle, or *core*, that remains is used to make a variety of other wood products. The new veneer is then cut into widths of 4 feet or wider, and the defective sections are either repaired or discarded. Uncut veneer can also be stored on huge rolls until it is needed.

The *slicing method* is mostly used for hardwoods, or when the appearance and beauty of the grain or wood species is important. After the log has been cut open and examined, it is then decided which *flitches*, or angles and segments of the log, will yield the finest grain patterns. At this point, the block is conditioned, heated, and placed into the slicing machine, which holds the block and moves it against the knife edge as the flitches or slices of veneer are cut. A worker removes the slices and stacks them in the order in which they were cut. This ensures proper color and grain matching when the veneer is finally used.

In most instances, the veneer flitches are then glued to a plywood or particleboard base; for architectural-grade materials, a solid wood base is required. In any event, veneer must also be applied to the back of the base to prevent warping, though it is not necessary that it match the visible veneer's grain.

Because of the beauty of the grain of sliced veneers, matching the edges of the grain is very important. Cut veneers are limited in width by the size of the trees from which they are taken. Most applications for veneers call for widths that are many times wider than an individual flitch, so they must be glued edge to edge to create the required width.

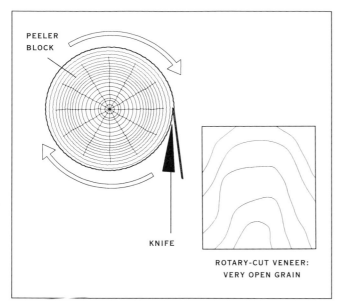

PEELER
BLOCK

KNIFE

ROTARY-CUT VENEER:
VERY OPEN GRAIN

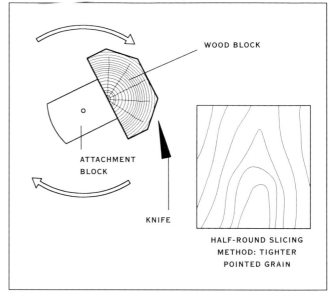

WOOD BLOCK

ATTACHMENT
BLOCK

KNIFE

HALF-ROUND SLICING
METHOD: TIGHTER
POINTED GRAIN

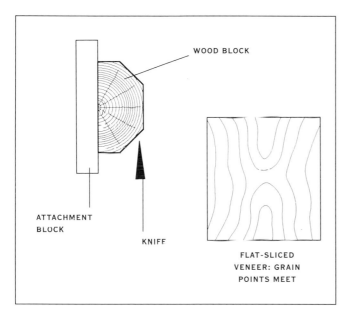

WOOD BLOCK

ATTACHMENT
BLOCK

KNIFF

FLAT-SLICED
VENEER: GRAIN
POINTS MEET

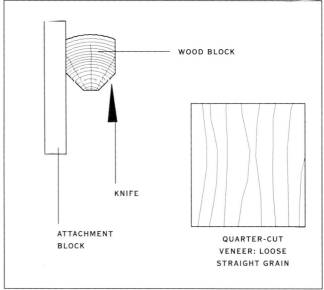

WOOD BLOCK

KNIFE

ATTACHMENT
BLOCK

QUARTER-CUT
VENEER: LOOSE
STRAIGHT GRAIN

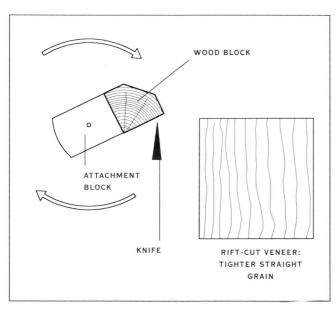

WOOD BLOCK

ATTACHMENT
BLOCK

KNIFE

RIFT-CUT VENEER:
TIGHTER STRAIGHT
GRAIN

VENEER CAN BE CUT FROM A PEELER BLOCK BY USING EITHER THE PEELING METHOD *(TOP LEFT)*, WHERE THE VENEER IS PEELED FROM THE LOG IN ONE CONTINUOUS ROLL FOR A VERY OPEN GRAIN, OR THE SLICING METHOD, WHERE THE BLOCK OF WOOD MAY BE TURNED ON THE LATHE TO CUT A VARIETY OF GRAIN CONFIGURATIONS: HALF ROUND *(TOP RIGHT)*, FOR A SOMEWHAT TIGHTER, POINTED GRAIN; FLAT SLICED *(ABOVE LEFT)*, FOR A GRAIN WHOSE POINTS MEET; QUARTER CUT *(ABOVE RIGHT)*, FOR A LOOSE STRAIGHT GRAIN; AND RIFT CUT *(LEFT)*, FOR A TIGHTER STRAIGHT GRAIN.

With the wide variety of veneer sizes, unmatched flitches can look disorganized. The task of matching flitches is further complicated by the interruptions in the grain, as result of the burls, crotches, and stumps that are taken from the areas around the roots or where the limbs meet the trunk. These highly figured areas are usually quite limited in size; some are as small as 12 inches square. Depending on the intended use of the veneer, these kinds of irregularities may be prized by artisans and woodworkers.

Methods of grain matching have been developed to greatly enhance veneer patterns. Generally, strips from the flitch are arranged so that the edge of one strip is aligned with that of the next to design a symmetrical pattern. The edges of the strip are aligned, the strips are taped together, and the assembly is then glued to a subpanel to create a matched plywood panel. To maximize balance, veneers are actually matched twice: initially during manufacturing, within each panel; then again during installation, between adjacent panels. Each matching pattern uses a different number and arrangement of veneer sheets to achieve the desired effect. While the process of creating patterns takes time and care, making matched veneer rather costly, the result is a beautiful and elegant finish.

THE CUT VENEER IS STACKED IN THE ORDER IN WHICH IT IS CUT IMMEDIATELY AFTER IT IS REMOVED FROM THE PEELER BLOCK TO FACILITATE GRAIN MATCHING LATER, EITHER IN AN ALTERNATING MANNER FOR A BOOK MATCH PATTERN *(TOP)* OR IN THE SAME DIRECTION FOR A SLIP MATCH PATTERN *(BOTTOM)*.

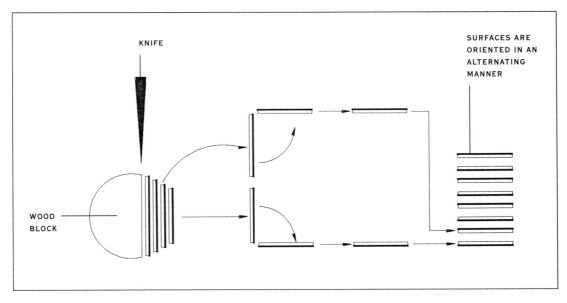

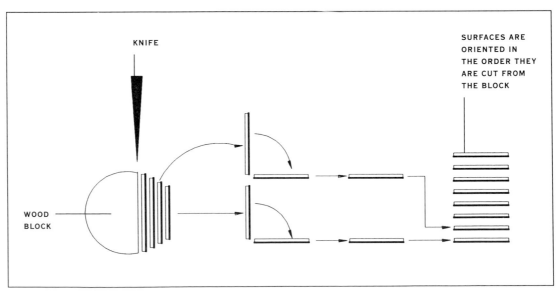

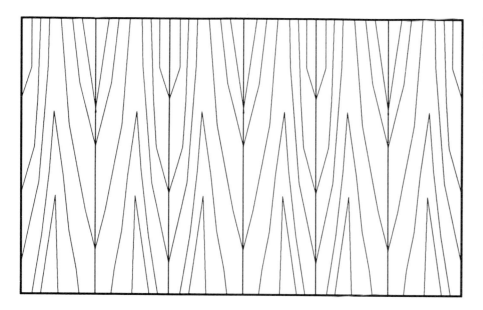

CUT VENEERS ARE
MATCHED IN A VARIETY
OF DIFFERENT PATTERNS,
INCLUDING BOOK MATCH
(TOP), REVERSE DIAMOND
PATTERN *(CENTER)*, AND
SLIP MATCH *(BOTTOM)*.

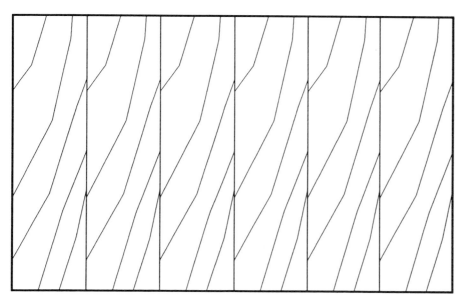

MANUFACTURING PLYWOOD

If veneer is not used to make matched panels, it can be made into plywood immediately after it has been cut and dried. Plywood is formed from thin layers of veneer that are glued together under pressure and heat. The grain of each layer of veneer runs perpendicular to those above and below it. The layers are placed into the slots of a press that applies the glue and compresses them at a specific pressure, which depends on the species of wood and the type of plywood that is being made. After a specified curing or setting time, the plywood panel is removed from the press and trimmed to its proper dimensions.

Plywood sheets are available in a wide range of thicknesses, from $3/32$ inch to $2^1/4$ inches; the most common are $1/4$, $3/8$, $1/2$, $5/8$, and $3/4$ inch. The thickness of the veneers or plys depends on the desired thickness of the finished sheet. The standard sheet size is usually 4×8 feet, although larger sizes are also produced. In many cases, the outer, visible plys are made from appearance-grade veneer. The inner plys' main requirements are that they can be securely bonded to the others and that the direction of their grain alternates at right angles. Most plywood sheets are composed of three to five plys, but more are used to make specialty grades. Short strips of solid lumber or particleboard that have been glued together side by side and overlaid with appearance-grade veneer serve as the inner plys of *lumber core plywood*, which is used primarily for casework and furniture. Although this type of plywood has improved edge strength, there is some loss in bending and torsion strength.

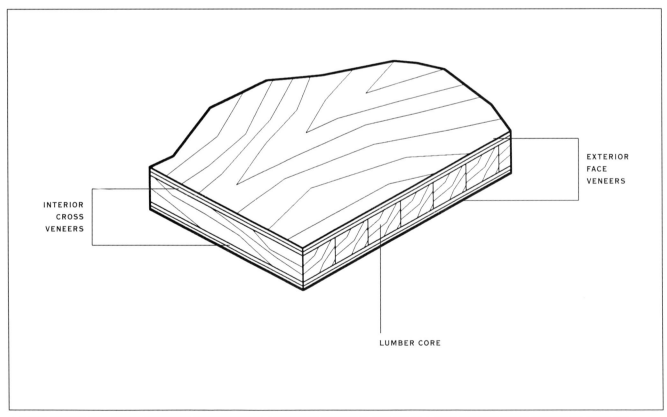

INTERIOR CROSS VENEERS

EXTERIOR FACE VENEERS

LUMBER CORE

A CROSS SECTION OF A SHEET OF LUMBER CORE PLYWOOD, WHERE THE VENEER IS APPLIED TO A CORE OF EDGE-GLUED BOARDS TO SIMULATE SOLID LUMBER.

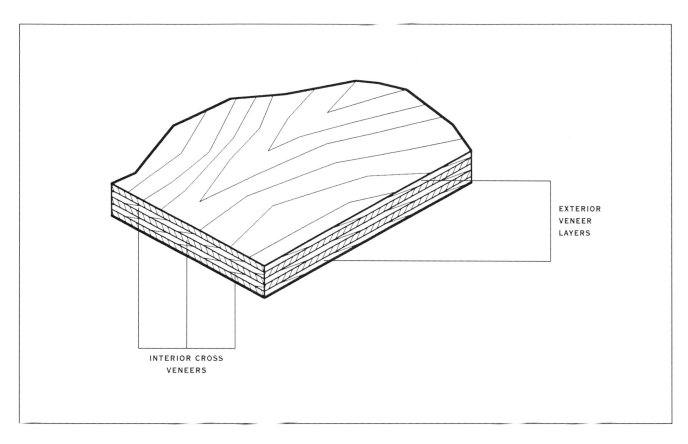

EXTERIOR
VENEER
LAYERS

INTERIOR CROSS
VENEERS

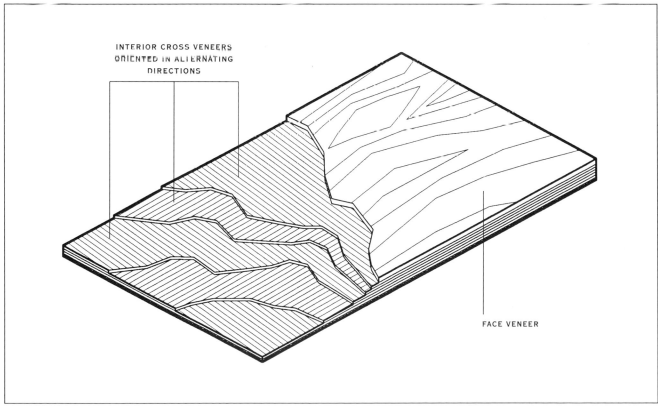

INTERIOR CROSS VENEERS
ORIENTED IN ALTERNATING
DIRECTIONS

FACE VENEER

CROSS SECTION VIEWS OF A TYPICAL SHEET OF PLYWOOD SHOWING THE ALTERNATING LAYERS OF VENEER GRAINS.

COMPOSITION BOARD AND PLASTIC LAMINATE

Particleboard, hardboard, and other similar products, which are generally referred to as *composition board*, are first cousins to plywood: They are manufactured in a comparable manner, using a similar type of press, glue, and application of pressure. But composition boards usually have only one ply, the entire thickness of which is sawdust or small wood chips that are bound together with a strong glue, which gives the panel its uniform strength. In general, composition board is less expensive than plywood.

Particleboard, which is composed primarily of sawdust mixed with a resin binder, is popular as an underlayment for floors and serves other utilitarian uses as well. When a veneer is applied to one or both sides, particleboard can also be used as a wall finish, and for furniture, casework, and other interior applications.

Hardboard is made of finely chopped and shredded wood-based materials that have been mixed with a resin or glue. The panel's smooth surface, which is usually brown, is formed against a smooth mold. The smoothness and strength of the surface can be enhanced by adding resin to it during manufacturing; the surface can also be textured to imitate wood paneling. Hardboard is more resistant to scratches and gouges than plywood.

Plastic laminate is related to composition board but is made in a different manner. Instead of wood chips or sawdust, plastic laminate is formed from multiple layers of *kraft paper*—a strong paper made from wood pulp—that are bonded together with a resin that dries extremely hard. The color of the surface is the color of the layer of paper directly below the top coating of resin, which is particularly hard and dense. Patterns of fabric or wood can be printed on the top sheet of paper before it is included in the laminate.

One of the notable features of plastic laminate is its brown edge. As it is installed over the substrate, any edges will either be concealed by an adjacent piece, trimmed and left exposed, or covered with some type of trim. Plastic laminate is installed by first cleaning the substrate, then applying a coating of adhesive to both the substrate and the bottom of the laminate. After a few minutes of drying time, the plastic laminate is pressed flat onto the substrate and the exposed brown edge is trimmed down with a router.

Recently, manufacturers have marketed a plastic laminate product known as *solid core laminate,* in which every layer of kraft paper is the same color as the surface and the resin is tinted as well. Following installation, the edge of the laminate is exposed but blends remarkably well with the surface.

Plastic laminate is primarily used on countertops and for cabinets, although it is occasionally used as a wall surface. Its main advantage is the variety of colors and patterns in which it is available. Plastic laminate also has some disadvantages. Because its panels are inflexible, it can only be installed on flat surfaces. Simple curves such as rolled counter edges and other radiused shapes are possible, but compound curves are not. Another disadvantage is that it can be easily scratched. However, most manufacturers have tried to eliminate this problem by improving the scratch-resistance of the resin coating. Plastic laminate featuring this material is now available in an ever-increasing variety of colors and patterns.

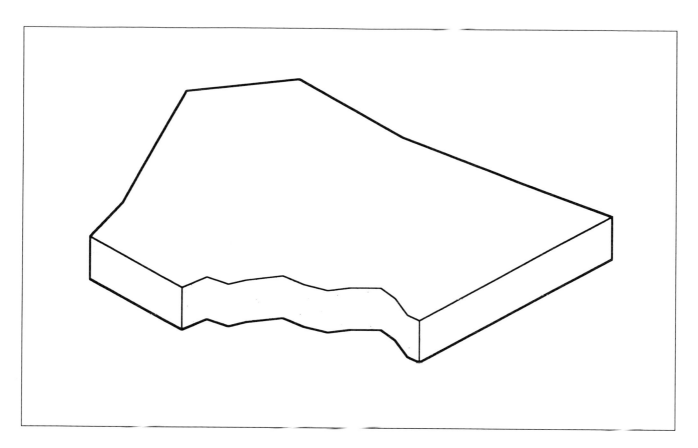

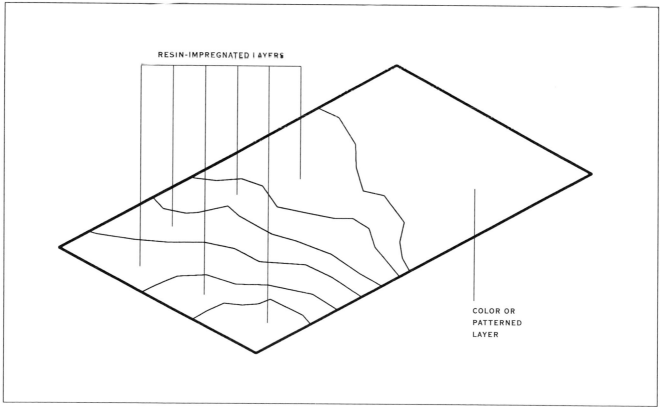

RESIN-IMPREGNATED LAYERS

COLOR OR
PATTERNED
LAYER

CROSS SECTIONS OF A SHEET OF PARTICLEBOARD *(TOP)* AND A SHEET OF PLASTIC LAMINATE *(BOTTOM)*.

WOOD FLOORING

Wood has been used as a flooring material for hundreds of years. Before the invention of the power saw and other electric tools, individual floor boards were sawn and sanded by hand, which made wood floors a luxury that only the wealthy could afford. As a result of these advances, wood flooring became quite common in the early twentieth century, though its popularity began to decline in the 1950s and 1960s, when affordable wall-to-wall carpeting was first introduced. Due to a renewed interest in natural materials, and because of its beauty and pattern variations, wood flooring made a strong comeback in the 1970s and remains popular today.

Both hardwoods and softwoods are used as flooring material. While less costly, softwood flooring's main limitation is that it generally does not wear as well as hardwood flooring, though it can be used quite satisfactorily in light traffic areas. Hardwood flooring's durability and variety in color and grain have contributed to its overwhelming popularity. White and red oak, beach, birch, and maple are among the hardwoods most commonly used for flooring.

TYPES OF WOOD FLOORING

Wood flooring can be installed in a variety of configurations, depending on the desired look. The simplest are the *plank floor* and the *strip floor,* both of which are designed to give a more or less linear look. Planks range in width from 4 to 12 inches; strips are usually 2 to 4 inches wide. Both ranges of board widths are installed in the same manner; with plank flooring, however, fastening the planks solely at the edges may not be adequate. Especially in widths approaching 12 inches, planks have a tendency to cup or bow in the middle. Therefore, in addition to nailing planks at the tongue, the installer countersinks screws to help hold them flat. These screws are inserted close to the ends of the planks (and in the middle of longer boards) to ensure a tight installation. For both strip or plank flooring, a variety of board lengths are used to achieve a random design.

Another type of wood flooring is the *parquet,* a pattern that uses many relatively short lengths of wood that can be arranged in almost any configuration. When first used, the parquet pattern was designed either by an architect or wood craftsman, and milled and installed by the latter. Today, most parquet patterns are premanufactured and preconfigured for easy installation. The most common premanufactured parquet size is 6 × 6 inches, usually made from oak. These squares are composed of 3/4-inch strips that are milled with thin tongue-and-groove edges and connected in a parallel pattern with small recessed metal wires. The squares are laid so that the length of the tile strips is perpendicular to the adjacent squares, which gives the finished floor a basketweave look. Parquet tiles are made in 12 × 12 inch squares as well as some specialty configurations. The variety of patterns available from a manufacturer is determined by supply and demand. Custom patterns are also available, but, due to nonstandard milling and installation methods, their costs are much higher.

Regardless of the shape of the wood pieces, the location and orientation of each piece on the floor as it relates to how it was cut from the log is critical. The pieces are cut in two different ways: *Flat-grained* or *plain-sawn flooring,* which is less expensive and has a more open grain, is cut with the width of the piece tangential to the circumference of the log; *vertical-grain flooring* is more durable because the wearing surface *is* the edge of the grain. Vertical-grain flooring also shrinks and swells less across the width, twists and splits less, and finishes better.

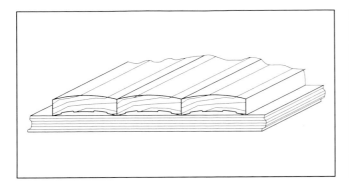

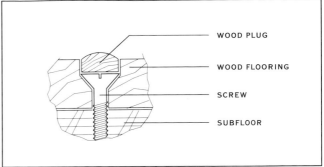

WOOD PLUG

WOOD FLOORING

SCREW

SUBFLOOR

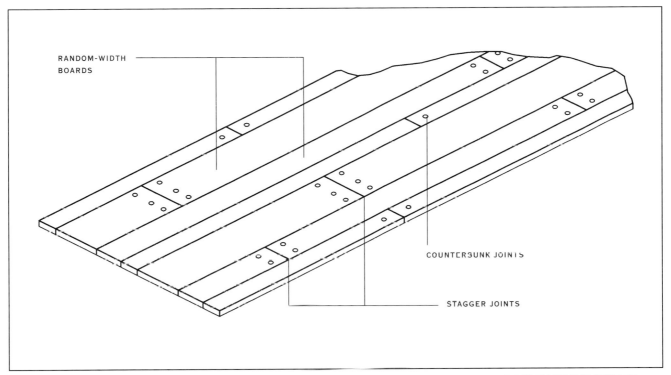

RANDOM-WIDTH BOARDS

COUNTERSUNK JOINTS

STAGGER JOINTS

BECAUSE PLANK FLOORING USES WOOD STRIPS OF VARYING WIDTHS, SOME OF WHICH APPROACH 12 INCHES, THE WIDER PLANKS MAY "CUP" OR WARP *(TOP LEFT)* IF THEY ARE NOT SCREWED TO THE SUBFLOOR WITH COUNTERSUNK SCREWS. THE SCREW HEADS ARE THEN COVERED BY WOOD PLUGS *(TOP RIGHT)*.

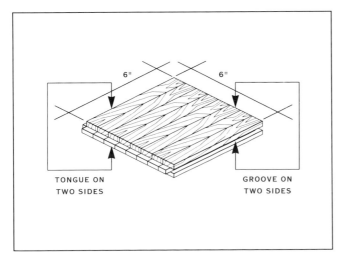

6"   6"

TONGUE ON TWO SIDES

GROOVE ON TWO SIDES

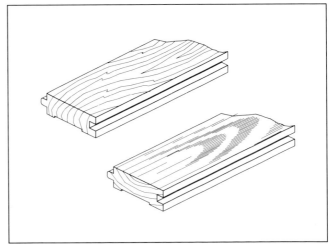

(LEFT) A TYPICAL OAK PARQUET TILE, WHICH IS USUALLY 6 INCHES SQUARE AND MILLED WITH TONGUE-AND-GROOVE EDGES. *(RIGHT)* AS WITH VENEERS, PLANKS AND STRIPS FOR FLOORING ARE ALSO CUT TO SHOW DIFFERENT GRAIN PATTERNS. SHOWN HERE FOR COMPARISON ARE TWO STRIPS OF FLOORING: FLAT-GRAINED *(TOP)* AND VERTICAL-GRAINED *(BOTTOM)*.

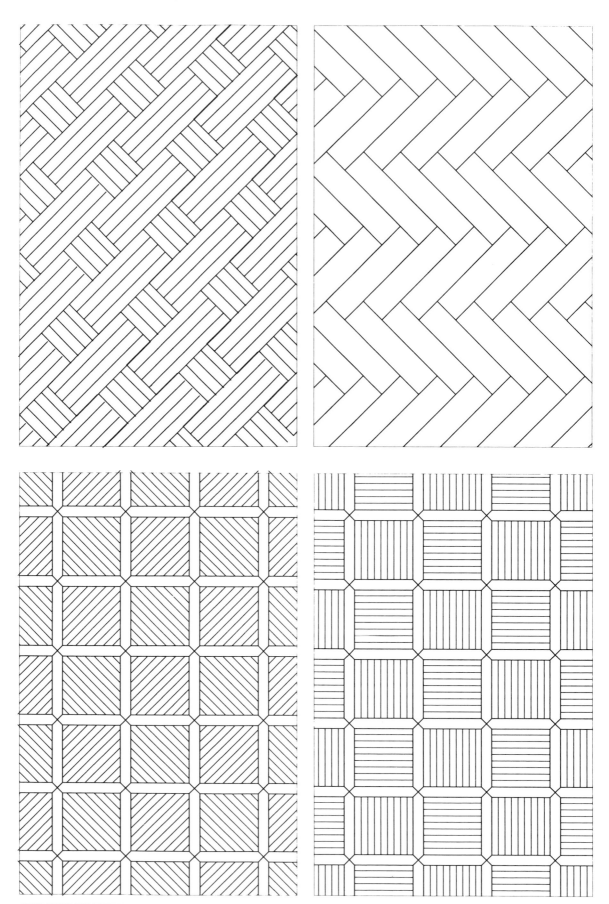

FOUR BASIC PARQUET FLOORING PATTERNS: TIMES SQUARE *(TOP LEFT)*, SET ON A DIAGONAL; HERRINGBONE *(TOP RIGHT)*;
SAXONY *(BOTTOM LEFT)*; AND MONTICELLO *(BOTTOM RIGHT)*. THE SAXONY AND MONTICELLO DESIGNS CAN INCORPORATE MORE
THAN ONE SPECIES OF WOOD. (NOTE THAT PATTERN NAMES MAY VARY AMONG MANUFACTURERS.)

FLOORING JOINTS

The way that the pieces of a wood floor are joined is as important as the types of wood used. While almost any common joint could be used to install a wood floor, there are a few that are simple and economical to use and still provide a sturdy joint.

The simplest joint type is the *butt joint*, which is made by placing two flat-edged boards together and nailing them to the floor. It is used mostly for unusual custom patterns, or for a species of wood or a grain pattern that is not normally used in flooring. While highly versatile, the butt joint's main disadvantage is that the nail heads are exposed and must be *set*—which means that the head of the nail is pounded down into the wood surface—and the depression filled with a wood filler. Also, floors installed with butt joints don't fit as tightly as those installed with other types of joints. The tightness of the joint depends upon how firmly adjacent boards can be held together while they are nailed down.

Considering these limitations, there are several flooring joint types that are preferable to the butt joint. One is the *doweled joint*. This joint is strengthened by a series of dowels drilled perpendicular to the length of the board and parallel to its surface. A variation on the doweled joint is the *spline joint*, which uses a thin strip of wood to accomplish what the dowels do: align and level the adjoining surfaces.

A variation on the spline, the *tongue and groove* is the most common type of flooring joint. In this joint type, the tongue and groove are milled as part of the opposite edges of the board, and are designed so that the tongue, which is nailed into the floor first so that the head of the nail remains hidden, squeezes tightly into the groove with only a careful, light tap with a mallet. To install tongue-and-groove joint flooring, the boards are simply laid out roughly in place, oriented to ensure that the same part of the joint on adjacent boards will not align, then tapped into place and nailed.

BASIC WOOD FLOORING JOINTS: A BUTT JOINT *(TOP LEFT)*, A DOWELED JOINT *(TOP RIGHT)*, A SPLINE JOINT *(BOTTOM LEFT)*, AND A TONGUE-AND-GROOVE JOINT *(BOTTOM RIGHT)*.

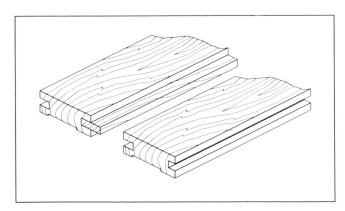

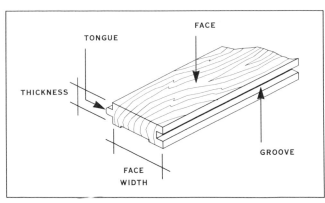

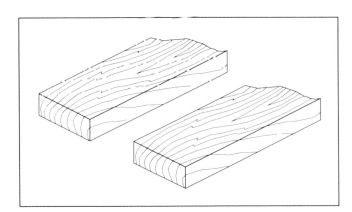

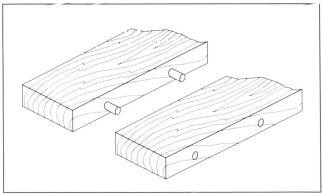

INSTALLATION

Because a floor usually receives more wear than other surfaces, one can see why the quality and longevity of a wood floor depends largely on the caliber of its installation. If a wood floor moves or flexes more than it should, its abnormal wear can result in expensive repairs.

Wood flooring can be installed using a variety of methods, which, in addition to the type of wood flooring, depend on the type of subfloor, which can be either *nailable* (built with wood strips, plywood, or particleboard underlayment) or *non-nailable* (made of concrete, stone, or brick).

With most parquet blocks or tiles, installation is quite simple. Assuming that the subfloor is level and dry, the flooring is installed with a mastic or spreadable adhesive that is spread evenly with a notched trowel in sections small enough to facilitate installation before drying. The tiles are then pressed into the mastic, pulled tightly against adjacent tiles, and then tapped into place. After a section or two has been laid, the tiles are rolled with a weighted roller to help set and level the floor.

There are a few other important points to keep in mind for parquet floor installation. First, the installer must leave a 1/4- to 3/4-inch gap or *expansion void* between the tiles and the wall around the entire perimeter of the room to allow the wood to expand without cracking or buckling. Also, as with any parquet-type flooring, the tiles must be laid starting at the center of a room, to ensure a balanced and centered installation.

A CROSS SECTION DRAWING OF A TONGUE-AND-GROOVE WOOD FLOORING INSTALLATION SHOWING THE SUBSURFACES OF THE ADJACENT WALL AND FLOOR. THE INSTALLER MUST LEAVE A 1/4- TO 3/4-INCH EXPANSION VOID BETWEEN THE FLOORING AND THE WALL IN ORDER TO ALLOW ROOM FOR THE WOOD TO EXPAND.

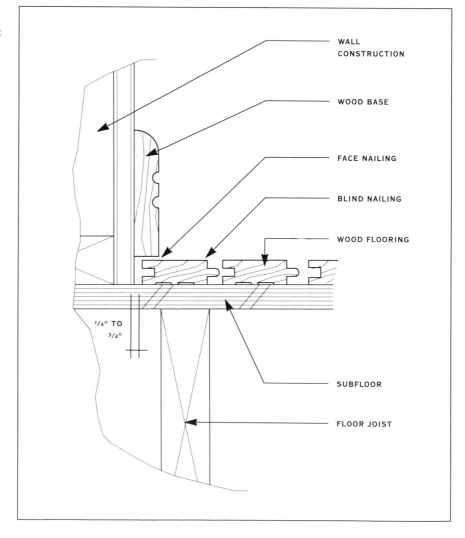

WALL CONSTRUCTION

WOOD BASE

FACE NAILING

BLIND NAILING

WOOD FLOORING

1/4" TO 3/4"

SUBFLOOR

FLOOR JOIST

PARQUET FLOORING
IS NORMALLY BEGUN
AT THE CENTER
OF A ROOM IN
ORDER TO ENSURE
ITS BALANCED
AND CENTERED
INSTALLATION.

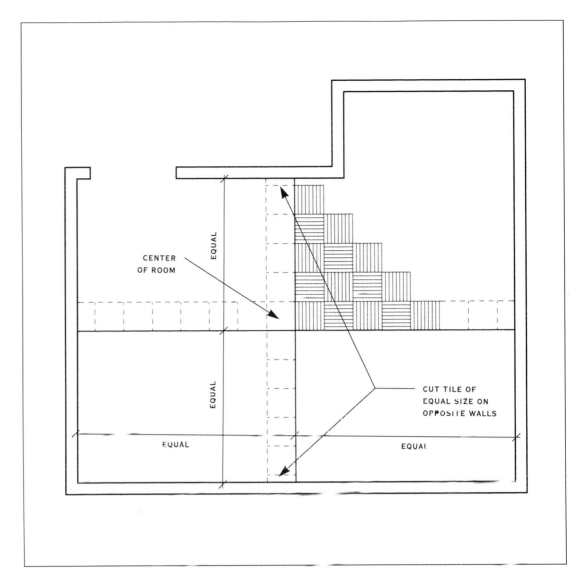

CENTER
OF ROOM

EQUAL

EQUAL

EQUAL

EQUAL

CUT TILE OF
EQUAL SIZE ON
OPPOSITE WALLS

Plank or strip flooring is installed by nailing, usually onto a concrete or wood subfloor. The latter is most often plywood or particleboard installed over wood joists or glued to a concrete surface. The traditional—and in many cases preferred—method of installing a wood floor over concrete requires *sleepers*, which are treated or preserved 2 × 4s of varying lengths (from 18 to 48 inches), are imbedded into hot asphalt mastic poured in long strips 12 to 16 inch apart across the floor. The sleepers provide the nailing surface for the floor and are installed at 90-degree angles to the strips or planks of the flooring. A polyethylene barrier is often laid over the sleepers to protect the flooring against moisture. Each wood strip is first tapped tightly into the adjacent board before it is nailed to the sleepers through the tongue. The strips should be of random lengths and installed so that no joints are aligned. Because the strips that are installed nearest to the wall cannot be nailed through the tongue, their face nails are set into the wood and the holes are filled.

Because the wider planks of wood tend to warp or twist, they require screwing to the floor at various points along their length. In many instances, plank flooring is manufactured with predrilled screw holes. The installer simply screws the plank into the subfloor, then glues the wood plugs over the screws to complete the installation. These plugs give a plank floor its distinctive look.

FINISHES

While the majority of wood floors are available from manufacturers already finished, many still require finishing. There are three steps required to finish a wood floor: (1) sanding, (2) inspection and filling, and (3) finishing.

Sanding is usually done with a drum-type floor sander, either with the direction of the grain for planks or strips and diagonally from the center of the floor for parquet or tiles. The edges and other hard-to-reach areas are sanded with a handheld sander. The first pass, or *cut*, made with the sander is done with a medium-grit paper; the final cut is made with a fine-grit paper. The floor is then inspected and cleaned to remove the wood dust. Any nail holes and cracks are filled with wood putty and sanded smooth. If desired, stain or bleach is applied at this point.

Finally, the finish is applied. There are two types of finishes: *Surface finishes* remain on the surface of the wood; *penetrating finishes* or *sealers* soak into the wood and seal its surface.

Polyurethane is the most durable of the surface finishes. It is composed of synthetic resins and plasticizers that wear extremely well and resist moisture, and is suitable for most commercial situations as well as areas that are subject to staining.

Varnish is the most common surface finish, with a durable, glossy luster that resists staining. It tends to scratch and darkens with age, making it somewhat difficult to blend repairs with surrounding older surfaces.

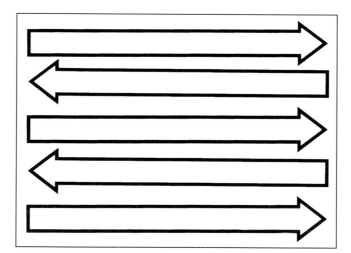

PLANK AND STRIP FLOORING *(LEFT)* IS SANDED FROM WALL TO WALL PARALLEL TO THE WOOD STRIPS, WHILE PARQUET FLOORING *(BELOW)* IS SANDED FROM THE CENTER TO THE EDGES.

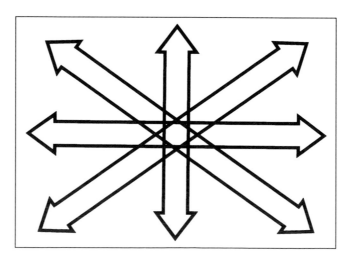

Shellac is easy to apply, dries quickly to a high gloss, and retains its original color well. Its main disadvantages are that it chips easily and spots if liquid stains are not cleaned up quickly.

Lacquer is very similar to varnish in its looks and wearability, but repairs can be made without a visible line between old and new applications because the new lacquer dissolves the old. Lacquer's main disadvantage is that it dries extremely quickly, making application difficult.

Penetrating finishes, which soak into the wood and then harden to seal and help protect it against stains and dirt, do not last as long as surface finishes and must be reapplied on a regular basis. Either a fast- or slow-drying sealer would be appropriate for a wood floor, and both require buffing to enhance its luster. Waxes can be applied over sealers if a higher gloss is desired.

As has been mentioned, all wood floors are subject to wear, and any preservative finish that is applied to wood must be refurbished from time to time. A variety of special wood products have been developed to prolong the material's life and finish, particularly in high-traffic situations.

In *acrylic-impregnated wood,* an acrylic resin is forced into the pores of the wood where, once dry, it has little affect on the look of the wood but greatly enhances its durability, giving it many of the same qualities as resilient flooring. In addition, the wood's grain tones, density, compression strength, acoustical qualities, and resistance to bacterial growth and flame spread are all augmented.

Foam-underlaid wood, which has a dense layer of foam rubber laminated to its underside, significantly increases the resiliency of wood flooring.

Depending on the requirements of a space, the increased cost of these products could be offset by their benefits.

CARE AND MAINTENANCE

If properly installed and finished, wood floors are quite easy to maintain. The designer should be aware of the following when advising clients about the care and maintenance of their wood floors.

1. The easiest task—and possibly the most important—is to keep dirt and dust off the floor. If allowed to accumulate, dirt and dust act like very fine sandpaper, slowly deteriorating the finish. A daily sweeping, dusting, or vacuuming, especially in high-traffic areas, is time well spent toward maintaining the look of the floor.

2. Waxing, which provides another protective layer of finish, also contributes to the long life of a wood floor's finish.

3. Use only solvent cleaning agents to clean a wood floor—NEVER use water. Water is a wood floor's worst enemy; even a newly finished floor may have small cracks and holes into which water can seep. There are many good cleaners on the market that are formulated to clean wood floors without using water.

4. Spills or stains should be cleaned up quickly: The longer they remain on the floor, the harder they are to remove. Tough stains can be removed by using a solvent cleaner and loosening the soil with fine steel wool.

The benefits of a regular maintenance program, which have been proven to extend the life of wood flooring, cannot be overemphasized.

WOOD PANELING

Used as a wall finish for centuries, wood paneling is still a very popular finishing material. There are two types of wood wall paneling: *solid wood* and *veneered plywood*.

Although solid wood and veneered plywood paneling are both high-quality finish materials, for many interior designers solid wood paneling is superior to veneered plywood paneling in both appearance and durability. While solid wood paneling may be more desirable, veneered plywood paneling enables interior designers to use woods and grain patterns that are otherwise unavailable or whose cost would be prohibitive.

PANELING JOINTS

Regardless of type, most wood paneling is classified by how it is milled and installed. One of the most popular is *tongue-and-groove paneling*, which is usually used for solid wood paneling. The way in which the tongue-and-groove edges are milled determines the look of the paneling: One technique butts the edges of the panels together, showing a thin line at the joint that subtly indicates the division of the boards; another, the *rabbet joint*, joins the boards in a small V, which puts a greater emphasis on the joint, and in some cases competes with the paneling itself for importance on the wall.

Another popular paneling joint is the *butt joint*. Because these joints are not as tight as tongue-and-groove joints, the look is casual and is most often used with rough sawn wood. A variation on the butt joint, the *reveal joint*, separates the edges of the panels with a space of about 1/8 inch to 1/2 inch. This type of joint brings the thickness of the wood into play by creating a shadow line between the panel edges. When the width of the space exceeds 1/2 inch, the surface behind the board becomes more important. A contrasting paint or wallcovering in this space will emphasize the joint in yet another way.

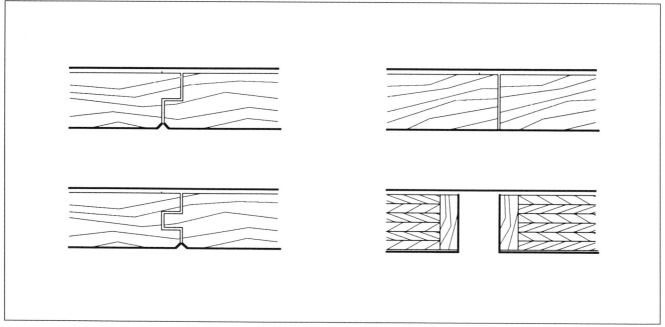

BASIC WOOD PANELING JOINTS: RABBET *(TOP LEFT)*, BUTT *(TOP RIGHT)*, TONGUE AND GROOVE *(BOTTOM LEFT)*, AND REVEAL *(BOTTOM RIGHT)*.

WOOD TRIM AND MOLDING

Small boards that are shaped to fit a specific or decorative purpose are called *trim* or *molding*. Trim, which is used to cover and conceal a joint, is usually made from wood or wood products and can be either ornamental or plain. Plastic and resin-based trims are used in conjunction with premanufactured casework, as a transition between the casework and an adjacent building element such as a wall, floor, or column.

There are two configurations of trim that are normally used: *standing trim* and *running trim*. The distinguishing characteristic of standing trim is that it is usually used in one-strip lengths, primarily around doors and windows. A standard door's height is usually less than a standard 8-foot strip of standing trim, so only one strip is needed to finish each side of the door. On the other hand, running trim is continuous in configuration. Baseboards, crown moldings, cornices, fascias, and wainscoting or chair rails are all examples of this type of trim. While reasonably long lengths of wood are sometimes available, the joints between pieces need to be minimized to maintain a continuous look. (Refer also to Chapter 13, "Casework and Trim," for information on custom trim.)

STANDING TRIM IS USED IN SPECIFIC CUT LENGTHS, USUALLY AROUND WINDOWS AND DOORS. IN THE CROSS-SECTION DRAWING ABOVE, THE DOOR STOP AND DOOR CASING ARE BOTH EXAMPLES OF STANDING TRIM.

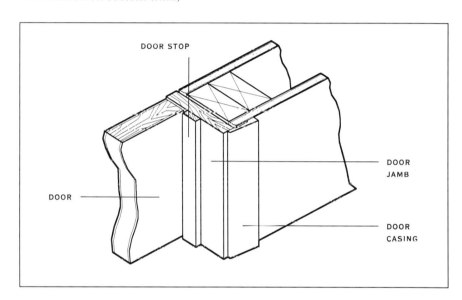

DOOR STOP

DOOR

DOOR JAMB

DOOR CASING

CROWN MOLDING, WAINSCOTING, AND BASEBOARDS ARE ALL EXAMPLES OF RUNNING TRIM.

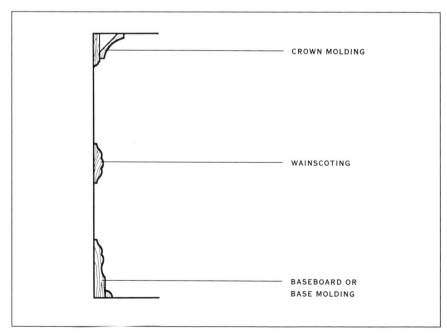

CROWN MOLDING

WAINSCOTING

BASEBOARD OR BASE MOLDING

3

STONE

STONE CAN BE USED AS A FINISH IN A VARIETY OF INTERIOR SPACES. ONE OF ITS MOST COMMON—AND MOST EFFECTIVE—APPLICATIONS IS AS A WALL AND FLOOR FINISH IN THE LOBBY OR RECEPTION AREA OF A COMMERCIAL BUILDING. *BUEHNER CORPORATION*

One of the earliest known building materials, stone has been used throughout history under a wide range of architectural and decorative circumstances, from the construction of basic shelters to the detailed ornamentation of both exterior and interior spaces. This beautiful and versatile material continues to successfully meet the demands of modern architecture and interior design. In fact, it was not until the mid-eighteenth century that other building materials, aside from wood, were used to any great extent.

The enduring popularity of stone is a result of its two most important characteristics: availability and durability. As a ubiquitous and integral part of the natural environment, it can be excavated and finished in a variety of surface textures. Along with its capacity to withstand the forces of nature, it can be shaped to build walls, columns, and other structures, offering diversity in the configuration of the built environment. Each type of stone, which is a reflection of the geological history of a particular locale, has its own specific set of physical characteristics: color, veining, texture, and hardness.

In layman's usage, the words "rock" and "stone" are interchangeable. In professional terminology, however, *rock* is used to refer to the natural material before it is quarried or processed, while *stone* refers to rock that has been removed from the earth and formed or shaped.

PROPERTIES OF STONE

All rock is classified into one of three geological categories—igneous, metamorphic, or sedimentary—which reflects how it was formed. *Igneous rock* is essentially solidified molten lava that has cooled and crystallized. How quickly the lava cools determines, in part, the stone's grain, texture, and further classification, for example, as granite, serpentine, or basalt.

Sedimentary rock, which covers about three-fourths of the earth's surface, is formed when loose material—sand, shell, minerals, and/or bone—that was suspended in a body of water accumulates in layers at its bottom. As a result of the weight of the water and of subsequent deposits of material, it gradually solidifies. These layers of material, which are referred to as *strata*, are what characterize sedimentary rock. Depending on its composition, sedimentary rock can be soft, hard, grainy, or densely formed.

Metamorphic rock is sedimentary rock that has been transformed as a result of heat, pressure, or mineral intrusions. For example, marble is limestone that has been highly crystallized; depending on the circumstances, sandstone can become slate, schist, or quartzite.

While the processes involved in the formation of rock and its composition are important, it is vital that interior designers understand the performance characteristics of *dimensioned stone*, which has been prepared specifically for use as an interior finish. As with many other finish materials, a stone's physical and aesthetic properties—such as how it will blend with other materials, and how it will look and perform after it has been installed—are also critical. A designer must be aware of how a stone's hardness and finish will affect a project, and use this information to enhance his or her design.

ABRASIVE HARDNESS

As an interior finish, dimensioned stone is used as a surface for floors and walls or as ornamental detail; it is sometimes also used to make furniture. Regardless of the application, however, a stone's *abrasive hardness*, or resistance to abrasion and general wearability, is of the utmost importance.

A stone's hardness is directly related to its composition. Dense stone such as slate, granite, and quartzite will usually wear quite well; softer stone, such as some sandstones, may not. Before specifying dimensioned stone, a designer and client should discuss the expected normal wear for the space in question. For instance, if the continual heavy foot traffic is problematic for a certain variety, other more suitable choices should be considered.

Typically, granite, slate, quartzite, and other fairly dense varieties of stone have excellent wearability. Marbles tend to be a bit softer, and sandstones are softer still. An informal rule of thumb relates a stone's wearability to its color. (Note that some slates and sandstones may not conform to this rule.) Generally, the more color a stone has, or the darker its color, the softer it is. Thus, white and light gray marbles tend to be among the hardest, while medium gray, mauve, blue, and pink marbles are a bit softer, and dark green, dark gray, red, and dark blue marbles tend to be the softest. A stone's comparative softness does not mean that it is entirely inappropriate as a floor finish. It is important, however, for a client to know, for example, that with constant, heavy foot traffic it will be difficult to maintain a polished surface on certain types of stone, and that after ten to twenty years some wear into the surface might be evident. This information may not necessarily prevent a client from choosing a particular stone finish. For instance, we have all seen marble stairs in older buildings that are rounded at the edges and are somewhat concave on the stepping surface after fifty years. They are no longer highly polished but they still perform and look quite well.

FINISH

As it applies to stone, the term *finish* indicates the appearance of the treated surface. Stone can be finished in several ways, each of which affects its color and pattern by either subduing or emphasizing them.

Polished. Probably the most popular, a polished finish is achieved by grinding and rubbing the surface of the stone with successively finer grades of abrasive materials until it is shiny or glossy. The richness of the stone's color and the fine details in its grain are made more prominent. A polished finish is not generally recommended for commercial floors.

Honed. A honed finish is obtained in much the same way as a polished finish, but the surface of the stone is rubbed until it is satin-smooth rather than shiny, and the color and pattern of the stone are somewhat subdued. It is recommended for commercial floors.

Rubbed. Also frequently referred to as a *matte finish* (similar to that in a painted surface), a rubbed finish is smooth without any gloss. While it does allow for occasional scratches, a fine rubbed finish should be free from any noticeable abrasions.

Rough sawn. As its name implies. a rough sawn finish gives the surface of the stone a slightly irregular but level surface in which the marks from the saw might still be visible.

Special finishes. These are several unusual finishes that each give a stone's surface a different look. A *flamed* or *thermal finish*, used specifically with granite, is a rough, irregular surface created by heating the stone to a high temperature, causing it to flake. A *sand-blasted finish* gives the stone a regular, rough texture. A *cleft finish,* which can be characterized by the phrase "irregularly regular"—meaning that the stone has an uneven but blunt surface—is obtained by splitting the stone at a natural weak point, usually at a layer or vein. Slate is particularly suited to this finish. This look can be achieved artificially on other varieties of stone by using other techniques.

STONE FINISHES: POLISHED *(TOP LEFT;* FLAMED OR THERMAL *(TOP RIGHT),* WHICH IS USED EXCLUSIVELY WITH GRANITE; AND CLEFT *(BOTTOM).*

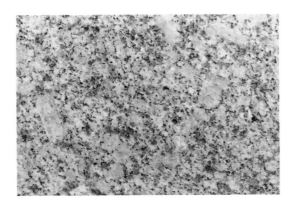
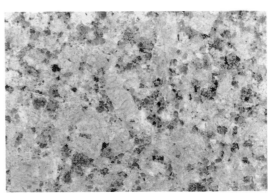

Regardless of its origin and relative physical properties, each variety of stone has its own set of specific physical characteristics.

GRANITE

An igneous stone, granite consists of a mixture of feldspar, quartz, mica, and hornblende, and has a granular appearance that is usually quite regular in pattern. Granites are classified by the size of the grain pattern—fine, medium, or coarse—which is in turn determined by the size of the minerals that compose the stone. Although granite is normally highly uniform in pattern, irregularities are still quite common. These irregularities, which are caused by an assortment of grain sizes or by a high concentration of minerals in a specific area of the stone, are expressed as veining and other random shapes. These attractive elements take shape during the rock's formation, while it is still in a semimolten state.

A granite's color—probably the most important feature that a designer considers when choosing it for a project—is determined by the color of the feldspar in the stone, although a large concentration of other minerals would also affect the color. The most common granite colors are grays, buffs, and pinks, as well as whites, blacks, greens, and reds. Granite is generally considered to be a hard stone, and can take and retain a high polish with moderate abrasion. Because granite is a natural material, the qualities that affect its strength—grain, texture, and veining—cannot be assessed until it has been removed from the ground.

For use as a building material, granite can be cut into huge blocks or cut and chiseled into a wide variety of shapes. For interior uses (either as a floor or wall surface), granite is most desirable in thin slabs that highlight its color or grain. The most common granite slab thickness is $3/4$ inch; larger panels may be cut to $1^1/4$ inches. (Depending on the need, thicknesses of $2^1/2$, 3, and $3^1/2$ inches are also available.) The length and width of a slab is, to a great degree, a function of its thickness. In other words, a long, wide panel will require a proportionately adequate thickness so that it will remain strong and stable. Therefore, a designer should bear in mind how the size and weight of a particular piece of granite relates to the design: Although it is possible to specify a 20 foot × 20 foot × 3 inch granite panel to fill an entire wall (its thickness is in proportion to its weight and size), its overall size would make it unmanageable in most interior spaces. A designer should expect to work with panel joints and try to take them into account when designing with granite. (See also "Sizes," later in this chapter.)

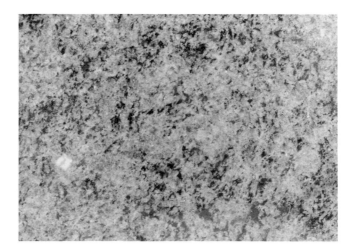

A FINE-GRAINED GRANITE WITH A FAIRLY REGULAR DARK-AND-LIGHT PATTERN.

MARBLE

Associated throughout European history with elegant interior design, marble is one of the most popular interior stone finishes. It is characterized by a wide range of colors, unusual and highly varied veining and shading, and other pleasing variations. Because the colors and patterns of a single type of marble differ from piece to piece, the method of installation is as important as the pieces that are chosen.

A metamorphic stone, marble is formed from a mixture of once molten limestones of somewhat differing compositions. The highly prized colors and textures associated with marble are a reflection of the minerals and other impurities that are introduced during its formation, and their brightness or intensity depends on the amounts of the minerals and how they mix with the surrounding material: Iron oxides cause pinks, reds, browns, and yellows; greens are formed from silicates, micas, and chlorites; and grays, bluish grays, and blacks are formed from petroleum-based materials. If much mixing takes place during the marble's metamorphosis, a somewhat consistent color and texture results; if the mixing is incomplete or uneven, the layers swirl into variegated veining patterns. While this incomplete mixing of materials is highly desirable, designers should be aware that veins can create weak points that might cause cracking or crumbling. A marble supplier can help to determine whether extensive veining will cause problems for a specific use.

CLASSIFICATION

Marble is classified into four groups that indicate, according to a marble's composition, the method of fabrication that is considered necessary and appropriate, based on trade practices established by the Marble Institute of America. This system of classification does not rank marbles with regard to hardness, color, or aesthetic value, but instead denotes the number and severity of faults, flaws, lines of separation, veins, and voids. These imperfections, which develop during the marble's formation as a result of the movement of molten masses, are not usually as strong as the surrounding material and, therefore, tend to crack or shear. As with a marble's color, these faults are a double-edged sword: While they are a significant aesthetic feature of the stone, each vein or fault contributes to the weakness of the piece. Designers first concern themselves with the look of a marble—its finish, colors, patterns, and other superficial physical characteristics. But it is also important to understand how the way a marble looks will affect its fabrication and installation.

A LIGHT-COLORED MARBLE WITH A MODERATE VEIN PATTERN.

Group A: These marbles are quite uniform in makeup, with no voids or flaws as a result of veining. Veins or swirls of different colors will usually be present, but the consistency of these veins is similar to that of the surrounding material. Therefore, Group A marbles are quite strong.

Group B: This group is similar to Group A, with some minimal voids and faults that can be corrected with a limited amount of waxing and sticking. *Waxing* involves filling small imperfections in the surface of the marble with shellac or other specialized compounds to make spaces level with the surrounding material. *Sticking* refers to the process of uniting two pieces of marble in a butt joint at a fault line.

Group C: This group encompasses marbles that have a greater quantity of flaws and voids, which require more waxing, filling, and sticking. It may be necessary to incorporate some forms of additional reinforcement during installation.

Group D: The marbles in this group have yet an even higher proportion of faults and veins, and are consequently harder to work with than those in group C.

At first glance, these designations may seem somewhat general and ambiguous; in fact, there are no exact criteria used to categorize each and every piece of marble into a particular group. While most interior designers will probably never need to classify marble, an awareness of these grades will prove helpful when working with marble artisans and installers.

SLATE

Slate, a metamorphic rock, is derived from the sedimentary rock known as shale, which is composed mostly of thin horizontal layers of clay. Through the process of metamorphosis, heat and movement fold, compact, and strengthen the layers, breaking them down into very small or fine-grained tightly overlapping particles. These many layers give slate its characteristic *face cleft,* which allows it to be split into thin sheets or veneers.

Because of the inherent inconsistencies of the metamorphic process, slate is available in a wide variety of textures, grains, and colors. When used to describe slate, the term "texture" refers to the ribbons of material that form its layers. These layers may vary in thickness from fractions of an inch to a few inches. Layers split from the same piece of stone may exhibit differences in texture, as they are more than likely not identical.

THIS SLATE TILE SHOWS THAT STONE'S CHARACTERISTIC UNEVEN SURFACE TEXTURE.

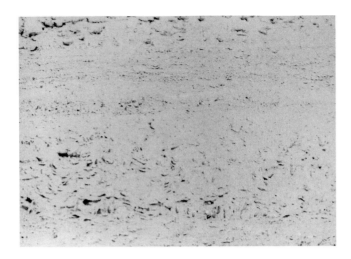

TRAVERTINE, A TYPE OF LIMESTONE, IS NOTED FOR ITS REGULARLY PATTERNED SURFACE, CHARACTERIZED BY HORIZONTAL PITTING AND POCKETS.

Although slate has a natural tendency to cleave in one direction, it may also sometimes split in another; the term "grain," as it applies to slate, refers to this second direction. This does not imply fragility; on the contrary, it reflects the layers of material that are in turn made up of many small overlapping flakes, which create an extremely strong, water-resistant bond.

As with other varieties of stone, a slate's color denotes its composition: The more common blacks, dark blues, and grays indicate the presence of carbon-based materials, while iron produces warmer hues, such as brown, purple, green, yellow, and red.

LIMESTONE

Limestone is a sedimentary stone that is composed primarily of calcium carbonate. Marble is the metamorphosed form of limestone. It is important to note that, commercially, most calcium-based rocks that are hard enough to take a polish are referred to as marble.

Limestone is classified by its density: Low-density limestone ranges from 110 to 135 pounds per cubic foot, medium-density limestone falls within a range of 135 to 160 pounds per cubic foot, and high-density limestone has a density of 160 pounds per cubic foot or greater. The strength of limestone depends on many factors, including the strength of the calcite crystals and of the binder between them. The limestones most commonly used as interior finishes are calcarenite, coquina, dolomite, crystalline, oolite, and travertine.

Once again, color is used to infer a limestone's mineral composition. Because it is sedimentary, limestone may also contain spots, fossils, shells, pit holes, and other elements that were incorporated into the stone before it solidified, all of which affect its look and texture. When used to describe limestone, the term "texture" refers to the size, degree of uniformity, and arrangement of minerals; variations in color and texture are considered desirable.

Limestone can be fabricated into standard sizes and thicknesses and finished in a manner similar to that used for marble.

SANDSTONE

Sandstone, a sedimentary stone, is composed of sand from the bottoms of prehistoric lakes and ponds that, following the addition of calcium carbonate, fused into a solid mass when the moisture evaporated.

THE LAYERS
CREATED DURING
ITS FORMATION ARE
CLEARLY VISIBLE
IN THIS EXAMPLE OF
SANDSTONE.

The hardness of sandstone depends on three conditions: the composition of the grains of sand, the strength of the bond between the sand and the "cement" of the calcium carbonate, and the degree to which the two elements have consolidated. Sandstone is available in a range of densities, from soft enough to crumble by hand to hard enough to be polished and used as flooring.

The type of sandstone that most people are familiar with is the brownish red variety known as *brownstone*, which was used as an exterior finish on many buildings throughout the United States in the late nineteenth and early twentieth centuries. Due to brownstone's softness, heavy, blocky veneers were used on exteriors because the standard dimensions for denser stone such as granite and marble were not appropriate. Brownstone and other softer sandstones are not commonly used as interior finishes.

Flagstone, which has a harder, durable texture that is more representative of most commercial sandstone, can be cut or split to give a cleft finish to flat surfaces. Its density and texture are somewhat similar to slate, and it can be used on walls or floors where slate might be called for. It also makes an attractive finish when used to construct a masonry wall. Although commercial sandstone is relatively hard, it still has its limitations. Interior designers should ask their suppliers to familiarize them with the characteristics of the varieties that are available.

QUARTZITE AND OTHER QUARTZ-BASED STONE

A metamorphic stone, quartzite is much harder and denser than the sandstone from which it developed, making it more suitable for use by the interior designer. It may have its surface finished in most of the textures mentioned earlier to give it a polished, flat, or textured look. It can be cut and fabricated in sizes and thicknesses common to most other stones.

Stone with a high percentage of quartz is almost entirely white. The presence of iron oxide causes red, while buff, yellow, and brown are formed by limonite. Because of its porosity, quartzite may fade or change color somewhat when exposed to weather, light, and moisture.

TERRAZZO

Rather than a specific stone variety, terrazzo is an *agglomerate* stone product. The mixture of *aggregate*—small or crushed stone particles—is set in a cementitious binder or matrix that is poured onto the substrate, smoothed out, and leveled. After the material has cured, it is usually ground smooth to produce an even walking surface.

A SEDIMENTARY-
BASED METAMORPHIC
STONE, QUARTZITE'S
COMPOSITION
IS HIGHLY
CRYSTALLIZED.

A terrazzo floor's colors also depend on the material's two primary components. The color of the aggregate is limited only by the variety of stone. While marble, quartzite, or granite chips are the most common, almost any variety can be used. The binder can be tinted to either complement or contrast with the color of the aggregate, and more than one pairing of aggregate and binder can be used in a single installation. Terrazzo patterns are generally determined by the shapes, general distribution, and sizes of the aggregate's chips, which range from about $1/8$ to 1 inch in diameter and can be mixed and matched to form a variety of standard or custom designs. Before the terrazzo mixture is poured, the floor area is divided into sections with *terrazzo strips*, which are bronze or zinc strips from $1/8$ to $3/16$ inch wide that are fitted at the bottom with galvanized fins by which they are attached to the subfloor (see also Chapter 5, "Metals"). The dimensions of the sections can vary from 4 to 10 or 12 feet, and though squares and rectangles are the most common, almost any configuration can be installed.

Terrazzo is extremely durable and requires little maintenance, which makes it particularly appropriate for such high-traffic areas as shopping malls and airports. While once extremely popular in the 1950s, terrazzo has recently made a modest comeback after losing some ground to carpeting and vinyl sheet flooring.

A COMPOSITE OF CHIPS OF MARBLE, QUARTZITE, AND GRANITE, TERRAZZO IS AVAILABLE IN FOUR CONFIGURATIONS: STANDARD, WHICH USES MEDIUM-SIZED CHIPS; VENETIAN, WHICH USES MEDIUM-SIZED AND VERY LARGE CHIPS FOR CONTRAST; PALLADIANA, WHICH USES RANDOMLY SCATTERED TINY, THIN CHIPS; AND RUSTIC, IN WHICH THE CHIPS ARE NOT LEVEL WITH THE SURFACE OF THE BINDER OR MATRIX. (NOTE THAT PATTERN NAMES MAY VARY AMONG MANUFACTURERS.)

STONE VENEERS

Although designers usually see stone only after it has been processed into its final, usable dimensions, it would be naive for anyone to think that it is taken from nature in sizes and shapes that approximate those used for finishes. In fact, stone in its natural state is so diverse that "standard" sizes and thicknesses can only be approximated.

Most stone is excavated from vast deposits in the ground and removed in large blocks. These blocks are cut so that they are large enough to allow for some flexibility for future use but small enough to be conveniently moved and handled. The blocks are then sawed into much thinner slabs, or *veneers*, which are more suitable for interior and exterior applications. Other dimensions are available for interior finishes, but the majority of stone is applied as veneer.

CUTTING VENEERS

Several methods are used to cut stone veneers. The most common uses a gang saw that has been fitted with a series of equally spaced diamond-tipped blades that slice the block into multiple slabs of veneer. Another method utilizes a stream of water mixed with abrasive compounds that, when directed at the stone under extreme pressure, quickly erodes small amounts of stone at the point of impact, thereby cutting a slab of a specific thickness.

With some varieties of stone, such as marble, the direction of the cut can affect the beauty of the finished veneer. As was mentioned earlier, as the layers of the stone are formed they may stratify into visible lines or swirls, which in the quarried stone can be either horizontal or vertical, angular or curved, depending on how its materials shifted or moved during formation. Sometimes the layers appear in concentric "puddles" known as *fleuri*. All of these characteristics affect the look of finished stone. When stone is cut across the "grain" or perpendicular to the bed (referred to as an *across-the-bed* or *vein cut),* the lines of its veins will be closer together and more regularly spaced; when cut with the "grain" or parallel to the bed (called a *with-the-bed* or *fleuri cut,)* the vein lines have a more open pattern; cutting across the veins at an angle will show still another look. Depending on the variety of stone, the configuration of the rock at the particular quarry, and past experience with different methods of cutting veneer, quarriers know which techniques will enhance the stone for the most desirable product.

(LEFT) A BLOCK OF STONE BEING CUT INTO SLABS OF VENEER WITH A MULTIBLADE GANG SAW. *BUEHNER CORPORATION.* (RIGHT) STONE VENEERS, WHICH ARE EASIER TO HANDLE AND MOVE THAN LARGE, UNPROCESSED BLOCKS, ARE SHOWN HERE STORED OUTDOORS IN A QUARRY, READY FOR FUTURE USE.

Sedimentary stone, which is formed in layers and has a natural cleft, does not lend itself easily to the cutting of veneer. Veneers of this type of stone are made by driving a wedge or other device between the planes of the stone's layers so that the stone cleaves at the closest natural stratum. In this instance, the thickness of each veneer can only be approximated—slabs can vary in thickness by ¹/8 inch or more—and the layers are not completely flat. Once installed, the transition between thicknesses is reasonably smooth, creating a distinctive, pleasantly uneven look.

SIZES

Depending on a stone's specific physical properties—density, hardness, fragility, proportion of flaws, and so on—and the relationship of the practical size of each piece to its thickness, veneers for most varieties of stone are usually available in a range of sizes and thicknesses. Generally, most are cut in ³/4-inch to 1¹/4-inch thicknesses, though thicknesses of 1¹/2 to 2 inches are not uncommon. For interior uses, the ³/4-inch thickness is the most popular. For thicknesses in this range, the length and width of the veneer can be as much as 8 × 5 feet. Larger sizes, which are difficult to handle, move, and fabricate, are mainly used as exterior cladding on buildings or in very large building lobbies. For interior projects, a panel's size becomes an element of the design and is related to other aesthetic considerations, such as the pattern of the stone and where and how its color varies. The number and size of faults or veins also have a bearing on panel size: When they differ in color, the strength of the stone is not diminished; extensive veining, voids, and other flaws result in weak joints and, in many cases, limit a panel's size. An interior designer should not proceed before contacting a supplier, who will be familiar with the limits of each particular variety.

Because of their relatively small size (8, 12, and sometimes 18 inches square), stone tiles can be cut to approximately ¹/4-inch thicknesses and still be workable. At that thickness, however, they must then be treated as tiles and installed with tile setting procedures; the strength of any tile flooring is derived to a great extent from its setting bed and the type of adhesive used.

STONE TILES ARE AN UNUSUAL FORM OF STONE VENEER IN THAT, DUE TO THEIR RELATIVELY SMALL DIMENSIONS, THEY CAN ONLY BE INSTALLED WITH TILE SETTING PROCEDURES, BOTH FOR FLOORS AND WALLS. *BUEHNER CORPORATION*

PATTERNS

Patterns in cut stone, which are a reflection of the natural conditions of the unquarried rock, are as varied as the stones themselves. They may take the form of lines, either ribbon thin or thick, that contrast with the surrounding material in color, texture, or both, or otherwise exhibit subtle differences. They may also take the form of concentric circles, shading, blotches, or shapes in a range of sizes. Even the apparent absence of a pattern is, in itself, a pattern.

Veneer patterns and their matching between panels are most commonly associated with marble. Related to the workable size and weight of the panels, most veneer patterns must be designed to account for joints or other transitional contingencies. The process and technique of matching veining patterns in marble veneer are quite similar to those used for grain in wood veneers, and terminology such as book matching, slip matching, and end matching also applies to stone veneers. Exact pattern matching is, however, not as easily accomplished. Because of the width of the saw blades, some stone is lost during the cutting process, which can mean, for example, that the pattern may not align exactly when attempting an edge-to-edge match.

When compared with wood veneers, it is readily apparent that the grain of even the most highly figured marble is not as regular and definite as that of wood. These irregularities and differences are part of its beauty.

THE FAIRLY REGULAR VEINING OF THIS STONE, WHICH WAS CUT PERPENDICULAR TO THE VEIN, OR ACROSS THE BED, CAN BE MATCHED RELATIVELY EASILY IN A SIDE SLIP, END SLIP, OR BOOK MATCH PATTERN.

INSTALLATION

The process of installing stone flooring is something of a hybrid, combining procedures common to both tile setting and masonry, and depends on the size of the stone tiles. The smaller stone tiles are installed in the same manner as ceramic tiles, and the setting bed supports the installation and strengthens it against cracking and breaking. For stone slabs, which are 3/4 inch thick or larger and resist breakage simply because of their size, the underlying setting bed is used only to level the stone and hold it in place. With slabs, however, the weight of the material becomes a major consideration, since the overall weight of the floor is substantial. A structural engineer should be consulted to ensure that the subfloor will support the additional weight. It is also important to note that stone slabs should be installed by a stone mason rather than a tile setter.

When installing stone onto a wall, weight becomes the primary consideration. As with floors, while stone tiles require only standard tile setting procedures, steps must be taken to adequately prepare the substrate for larger tiles or thick slabs, which usually means that a plywood substrate is first installed onto the wall studs. The stone is then attached to the plywood by gluing the slabs to the wall surface with a series of circular dollops of adhesive, which are applied near each corner and at the center of where each slab will be positioned. The slab is then pressed onto the substrate, which holds it in place. The amount of adhesive used for this procedure is extremely important, as too little will simply not hold the slab on the wall and too much may increase the cost of the installation. Adjacent slab panels are installed in the same manner, and the joints are either grouted with a fine-grained grout or "caulked" with a flexible sealant. While the size of the joint can vary, most desigers choose to minimize them in order to keep the emphasis on the stone. With extremely large or thick panels, a system of metal fasteners using wires or strips is necessary.

Regardless of the method of installation, the installer will follow the guidelines that have been established and followed for many years by those in the profession. If the interior designer feels that additional guidance is required, a structural engineer can provide objective advice.

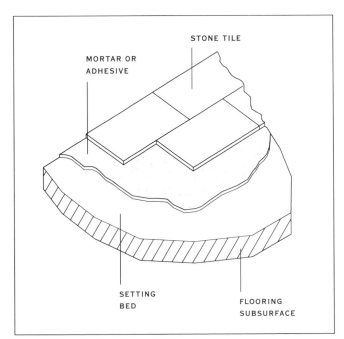

A CROSS SECTION DRAWING SHOWING A STONE FLOOR INSTALLATION.

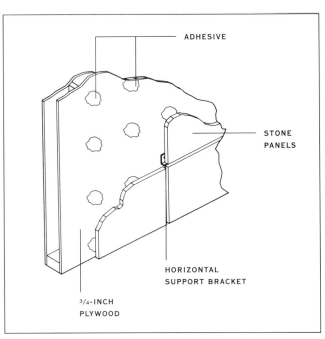

A CROSS SECTION DRAWING OF THE INSTALLATION OF A STONE WALL SHOWING THE DOLLOPS OF GLUE APPLIED TO THE SUBSTRATE.

4

BRICK

COMPLEMENTING THE INDUSTRIAL FEEL OF THIS RENOVATED SPACE, THE INTERIOR SURFACES OF ITS STRUCTURAL BRICK WALLS WERE SANDBLASTED. *ONSITE OFFICES, LOS ANGELES, CALIFORNIA; RODNEY ROSS, DEBORAH RACHLIN, PRINCIPALS*

The oldest form of unit masonry, brick is also one of the oldest man-made building materials. Brick walls dating from 4000 B.C. reveal that the ancient Egyptians, the Babylonians, and pre-Columbian Amerindians made their sun-dried bricks with sandy clay soil bound with straw and water. The main liability of this early brick was its tendency to erode when subjected to harsh weather, particularly rain.

In the seventh century B.C., the Babylonians first discovered that brick hardens and becomes impervious to water when fired at relatively high temperatures, and that the color, texture, and strength of brick are the direct result of its composition, dimensions, and firing time and temperature. These variables are still used to create the wide variety of bricks that are currently on the market.

From the first, brick was intended as a building material and used almost exclusively for that purpose. Because additional time, labor, and expense were necessary to cover the interior face of an exterior wall, much early architecture made use of exposed brick as an interior finish. Any additional handling, which usually involved painting or carving, preserved rather than concealed the identity of this familiar material.

Because interior designers are primarily interested in a material's appearance, pattern, and wearability, the structural aspects of brick are not covered in this chapter in depth. As with all finish materials—and in spite of brick's renowned durability—designers are encouraged to do further research by consulting the brick manufacturer or with an engineer if it will be used in any way that might result in unusual or abnormal stress or wear.

BRICK MANUFACTURING

Before the manufacturing process begins, a specific amount of water is added to sifted clay, depending on which method is used.

Soft mud process. The oldest method of brick manufacture, the soft mud process involves forcing wet mud into wooden molds to form the bricks, which when finished are referred to as *wood-molded* or (somewhat inaccurately) *hand-molded*. Once used to make bricks by hand a few at a time, this process is now mechanized and used mostly with clays that require a higher-than-average amount of water for mixing. Depending on the material that is used to lubricate the molds—either sand or water—the face texture of the brick can be either slightly roughened *(sand struck)* or smooth *(water struck).*

Stiff mud process. The most common method used to manufacture bricks today, the stiff mud process requires that the raw material of the brick first be tempered with water and blended thoroughly to produce a mixture that is quite stiff. The mixed clay is then extruded through a die of a specific size, creating a long horizontal column of molded brick. Using a taut wire as a cutting tool, the column is sliced evenly into individual bricks.

Dry press process. This method uses clays that, when wet, are still relatively dry and less plastic. In a hydraulic press, the only slightly dampened clay is compressed into brick molds under high pressure. Bricks made by this process—which is commonly used to make *face brick* (intended for the exterior or exposed surface of a wall—are very dense, strong, and precisely formed.

To reduce drying time, allow for a more even distribution of kiln heat, and improve the bond between brick and mortar, many bricks, particularly those intended for wall surfaces where only the *header,* or narrow end, will be visible, are manufactured with vent holes through the middle. Bricks made without holes, such as brick pavers (discussed opposite), give the designer much more flexibility in their orientation during installation.

After the unfired or *green* bricks are inspected and stacked onto special pallets or *cars,* they are then ready to be sent to the kiln for *predrying,* which minimizes cracking and warping, and *burning,* which, depending on its duration, determines in part the hardness and color of the finished brick. The bricks are loaded onto steel cars and slowly moved through the entire length of the kiln, whose speed and temperature are usually controlled by computer. The temperature range of the predrying section is 100 to 400°F; the bricks are burned at an average of 2000°F. As the bricks approach the exit of the kiln, the temperature is reduced slowly to prevent cracking and other imperfections. A pass through a brick kiln usually takes an average of 32 to 38 hours. The bricks are then allowed to cool completely before they are stacked and banded together in quantities of approximately 500.

THE PROCESS OF MANUFACTURING BRICK. SHOWN HERE ARE TWO OF THREE METHODS USED: THE SOFT MUD, WHERE THE BRICKS ARE FORMED IN WOODEN MOLDS; AND THE STIFF MUD, WHERE THE BRICK IS EXTRUDED IN ONE CONTINUOUS COLUMN WHICH IS THEN CUT INTO INDIVIDUAL BRICKS WITH A SHARP WIRE. THE GREEN BRICK IS THEN STACKED ON STEEL CARS AND MOVED THROUGH THE KILN IN THREE STAGES: DRYING (AT A RELATIVELY LOW TEMPERATURE), BURNING (AT AN EXTREMELY HIGH TEMPERATURE), AND COOLING (ONCE AGAIN, AT A REDUCED TEMPERATURE). THE FIRED BRICKS ARE THEN COOLED COMPLETELY, STACKED AND BANDED TOGETHER IN QUANTITIES OF APPROXIMATELY 500, AND STORED UNTIL NEEDED.

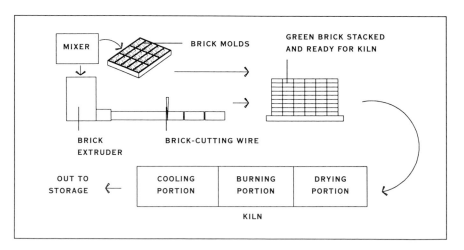

BRICK TYPES AND SIZES

Brick is manufactured in a wide range of sizes and types, each of which is intended to satisfy particular construction requirements and fulfill specific design needs. An interior designer should be at least generally familiar with the terminology in order to better advise his or her clients. All are available in fairly standard sizes (refer to the table below).

Common brick. The term "common" refers to a specific size of $2^5/8 \times 3 \times 8^5/8$ inches. Of all brick types, common brick is the most widely used for construction.

Modular brick. Made to more exacting standards, the size and color of modular brick are strictly controlled. If a designer requires a close tolerance of color or more exact mortar joints, modular brick is the logical choice. Modular bricks are usually used as face bricks.

Fire brick. Containing a high percentage of alumina, silica, or feldspar, fire brick is somewhat softer than common brick. It is commonly used for fireplace interiors or in other areas that are subjected to intense heat. Its colors tend to be in the beige range.

Brick pavers. These bricks, which are in essence a thinner version of modular brick, are used as a decorative wall facing and as flooring. In order to establish an adequate walking surface, only the sailor surface of the brick is installed. There are a few brick paver variations that are available, including the *split paver,* which is half the thickness of a standard paver, allowing the designer the option of brick flooring whose weight is substantially reduced. Brick pavers can also be produced in other special sizes, shapes, and colors.

Other standard sizes. The term "standard" refers to a set of generally established sizes, including modular, Norman, Roman, Atlas, fire, and various others.

Variations. Each type of brick can be manufactured for variations in texture and color. For distinctive textures, bricks can be roughed, combed (with either vertical or horizontal lines scored into the surface), or otherwise patterned.

MOST COMMONLY USED BRICK SIZES			
NAME	**HEIGHT** (IN INCHES)	**WIDTH** (IN INCHES)	**LENGTH** (IN INCHES)
COMMON OR STANDARD	$2^5/8$	3	$8^5/8$
MODULAR	$2^1/4$	$3^5/8$	$7^5/8$
NORMAN	$3^1/2$	$3^1/2$	$15^1/2$
ROMAN	$1^1/2$	$3^1/2$	$11^1/2$
ATLAS	$3^1/2$	$5^1/2$	$15^1/2$
MODULAR WITH CONCRETE BLOCK	$3^1/2$	$7^1/2$	$15^1/2$
FIRE	$2^1/2$	$4^1/2$	9
PAVER	$2^1/4$	4	8
SPLIT PAVER	$1^1/8$	$3^5/8$	$7^5/8$

NOTE: BECAUSE STANDARD INDUSTRY-WIDE SIZES HAVE NOT YET BEEN ESTABLISHED, DESIGNERS SHOULD CHECK WITH INDIVIDUAL SUPPLIERS FOR THE EXACT DIMENSIONS OF THEIR PRODUCTS.

In a process similar to that used for pottery, the face of the brick can be sprayed with a glaze before firing to create a hard, glasslike surface in a wide range of colors. Materials such as *grog,* which are chards of fired ceramic that provide shimmering glasslike effects, or iron filings for speckled textures, can also be added.

Designers should understand the importance of specifying the appropriate brick for a particular job, and how each size of brick can be used to achieve a particular look. For instance, Roman brick, which is about 30 percent longer and 30 percent thinner than common brick, might be used to enhance the length of a wall.

BRICKS ARE AVAILABLE IN A WIDE VARIETY OF SIZES, SHAPES, AND COLORS, EACH OF WHICH SERVES A SPECIFIC FUNCTION, EITHER FOR CONSTRUCTION OR DESIGN. *INTERSTATE BRICK COMPANY, WEST JORDAN, UTAH*

SOME COMMON BRICK TEXTURES *(TOP TO BOTTOM, FROM LEFT TO RIGHT):* COMBED, SANDED, CUT, SMOOTH, WIRE CUT, AND ROUGH TEXTURED.

BLOCKS

Blocks are masonry units that are equal in height to about three brick *courses*, or rows, approximately 7⅝ inches. Concrete block, glass block, and atlas brick, which is larger than brick but made of the same material, are all examples of blocks.

CONCRETE BLOCKS

A close relative of the brick, the concrete block is composed of concrete mixed with cinders, pumice, and other similar aggregate materials. It is primarily used to build economical structural walls. Since manufacturers have varied the basic concrete block by adding colored glazes and producing it in a variety of shapes and face finishes (ribbed or split, fluted, scored, and shadowal), it can now be used more often as an interior finish. However, due to its widespread utilitarian use, most clients remain unconvinced of the aesthetic charisma of concrete block.

GLASS BLOCKS

Glass blocks are nonload-bearing masonry units formed from two glass panels that are fused together to create a hollow unit that is approximate in thickness to a modular brick. The edges of the block are coated with a material that enhances the bond between the unit and the mortar. This strong, durable form of unit masonry is most intriguing for the possibilities it offers to diffuse light, ranging from translucent to nearly opaque. It is installed by a brick mason using the same procedures required for brick.

Glass blocks are made in a wide range of sizes, the most common being 6 × 6, 8 × 8, and 12 × 12 inches. In addition to the standard square, special shapes intended for edges, corners, and other treatments are produced. Most glass blocks are patterned on the inner surface—from waves to crosshatched scoring—leaving the outer surface smooth and easy to clean. Glass blocks can also be coated with reflective materials or colored with a wide range of dyes. Solid glass units are also available, to enhance security in wall installations or for use as flooring.

ALTHOUGH THEY
REQUIRE
CONSTRUCTION
TECHNIQUES
SIMILAR TO THOSE
USED FOR BRICKS
AND CONCRETE
BLOCKS, GLASS
BLOCKS ARE
NEVER USED FOR
STRUCTURAL
PURPOSES.
*PC GLASS BLOCK®
PRODUCTS,
PITTSBURGH
CORNING
CORPORATION*

MORTAR JOINTS

All forms of unit masonry are set in *mortar,* a paste made of portland cement, lime, water, and aggregates that "glues" each brick to the next and holds the wall together. The degree of adhesion between the brick and the mortar is called the *bond;* this term is also used to refer to the pattern that is used to construct a brick wall of more than one *wythe,* or brick, in width.

Because the strength of the mortar in holding the assembly together is essential to the wall's stability, interior designers should specify the type of mortar and the installation of the structure only after obtaining the advice of an engineer or a brick supplier. However, speaking strictly from an aesthetic point of view, designers can consider both mortar and joint as elements of a brick wall's design.

The way in which a mortar joint is finished (referred to as *striking a joint)* has an important effect on the design of a brick wall. Each type of joint has its own look, creating a distinctive shadow both on the brick and within itself. While the joints of exterior walls must be tooled to include a shelf that increases water resistance, any type of joint can be used on interior walls. In addition, normal mortar, which is gray, can be colored to either complement or contrast with the color of the brick.

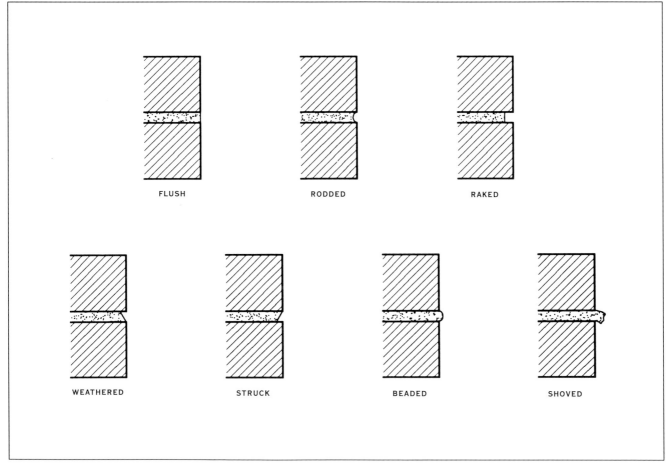

A SELECTION OF MORTAR JOINTS *(FROM TOP LEFT):* FLUSH, RODDED, RAKED, WEATHERED, STRUCK, BEADED, AND SHOVED.

BRICK PATTERNS

The choice of brick pattern depends on which surface is being finished. Wall patterns are derived from the configurations that were developed when masonry was used as a structural element first and for appearance second. The most popular—and one of the simplest to install—is the *running bond,* where the brick above covers the joint of the two bricks below. In a *stacked bond,* where the bricks are simply stacked one on top of the other, the mortar is an integral part of the structural integrity of the wall. In the *Flemish bond,* which was developed to strengthen exterior walls that are more than one wythe, the first six courses of brick are laid up in a common bond and the bricks of the seventh course are positioned as headers. A variation of the Flemish bond is the *English bond,* where the header bricks are spaced so that they form a cross shape within the larger pattern. When used as a flooring material, the look can take precedence over the need for structural stability.

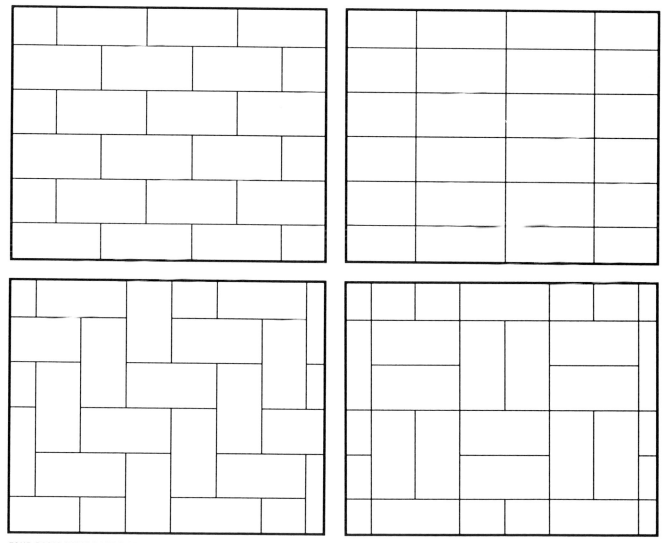

FOUR BASIC BRICK BONDS OR PATTERNS: COMMON *(TOP LEFT),* STACKED *(TOP RIGHT),* HERRINGBONE *(BOTTOM LEFT),* AND BASKETWEAVE *(BOTTOM RIGHT).* ONE OF THE BASIC STRUCTURAL BOND PATTERNS, THE COMMON BOND IS USED AS THE BASIS FOR SEVERAL OTHERS, BOTH STRUCTURAL AND NONSTRUCTURAL: RUNNING, FLEMISH, ENGLISH, AND ENGLISH CROSS. BECAUSE IT DOES NOT INCORPORATE AN INTERLOCKING WYTHE, THE STACKED BOND IS USED MAINLY FOR BRICK VENEERS. THE TWO BONDS AT BOTTOM ARE PRIMARILY USED FOR BRICK FLOORING INSTALLATIONS.

INSTALLATION

The installation of brick is a simple but exacting process. The main requirement is that the surface be level and plumb. If the mason squares and levels each course and ensures that all of the joints are a consistent thickness, the final result will be both structurally correct and aesthetically pleasing. It should also be noted that clean drinkable water should be used to mix the mortar, and that any extra mortar should be cleaned from the installation before it sets completely.

The initial procedure involved in installing a brick floor is the same as that required for ceramic and stone tile, in that a mortar bed on which the brick will be installed must be established first (see Chapter 6). In contrast to tile setting, however, the mortar and brick surface are established at the same time, as each brick is laid. The mortar is spread on the back and sides of the brick, which is then placed and leveled in its final position. A straight-edge is used to ensure that all the bricks are flush with one another. Once a section is completed, the excess mortar is scraped off and the joints are raked smooth and flat to prevent tripping and the accumulation of dirt. The process is repeated until the entire floor is finished.

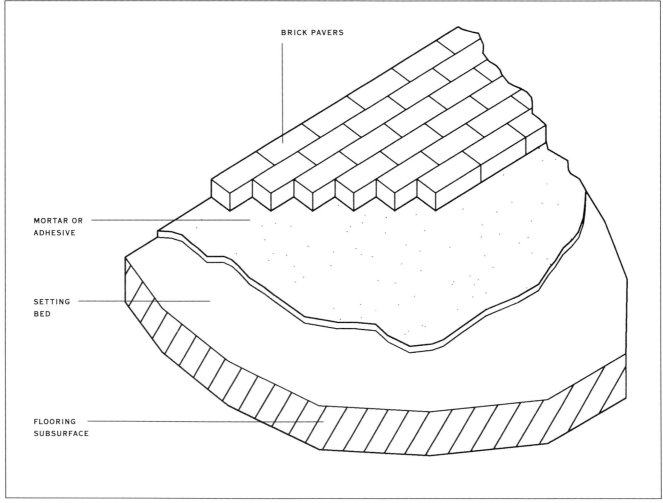

BRICK PAVERS

MORTAR OR
ADHESIVE

SETTING
BED

FLOORING
SUBSURFACE

CROSS SECTION DRAWING OF A BRICK FLOORING INSTALLATION.

Brick flooring can also be installed without mortar joints. The brick is simply laid tightly together on a flat level concrete surface. Sand is then continuously brushed over the bricks until any remaining spaces between them are filled. This type of installation, which creates a surprisingly tight floor, is most appropriate for exterior surfaces, or for interior surfaces that are subject to only light or moderate traffic.

To build a brick wall, the mason "butters" each brick with mortar on the bottom and one side, then presses it into place and levels it. This process is repeated until the course is complete. In succeeding courses, the mason may stretch a piece of twine along the top edge to confirm that it is level and flat.

In addition to soliciting the advice of engineers and brick manufacturers, the interior designer must also rely on their mason's ability to ensure the integrity of the walls' construction. In some cases, it may be possible to specify brick walls when working with an architect during a building's inception. In any event, unless it is used appropriately, the charm and usefulness of this finish may, sadly, be lost.

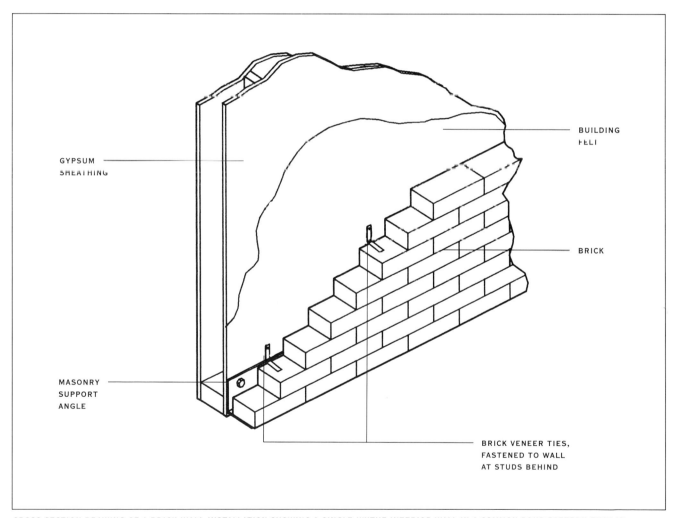

GYPSUM
SHEATHING

BUILDING
FELT

BRICK

MASONRY
SUPPORT
ANGLE

BRICK VENEER TIES,
FASTENED TO WALL
AT STUDS BEHIND

CROSS SECTION DRAWING OF A BRICK WALL INSTALLATION SHOWING A SINGLE-WYTHE INTERIOR WALL IN A COMMON BOND PATTERN THAT IS CONNECTED TO THE PLASTER SUBSTRATE WITH VENEER TIES.

5

METALS

THE UNIQUE USE OF METALS AS BOTH MAJOR AND MINOR DETAILING IN THIS APPAREL AND ACCESSORIES STORE ENERGIZES THE SPACE. THE VAULTED CEILING IS CONSTRUCTED OF BENT PERFORATED METAL PANELS ON A STEEL FRAME, AND THE TRIM ON THE SCARF RACK AND DRESSING ROOMS IS BURNISHED STAINLESS STEEL. *ALAN SCHINDLER PHOTOGRAPHY; COURTESY OF DORF ASSOCIATES*

Metals—specifically, iron and steel—have been used extensively in the structural systems of buildings since the advent of the Industrial Revolution. Metal fasteners, including nails, screws, and other tying elements, have been used in stone and masonry buildings since the classical periods of Greece and Italy. Although on a somewhat limited scale, metals have also been used throughout history by artisans who shaped them to fit a specific function or location.

The use of metal as an interior finish material, however, is relatively recent. Following the successful mass production of industrial-use metals, iron was precast into intricate decorative shapes such as columns, arches, canopies, and bases that were installed onto building facades. In addition, *tinplate*, which is a thin sheet of iron or steel that has been coated with tin, was shaped by pressing onto decorative forms and used as wall or ceiling ornamentation. *Wrought iron*, which is iron that has been further strengthened through forging, was used in both interiors and exteriors in a variety of forms, including stair and guard railings and column covers.

Because of their strong association with the late Victorian and prewar periods, many of these interior uses of metal were abandoned by the adherents of the Bauhaus and the International Style. Within the diversity and unabashed enthusiasm for surface textures that characterizes late twentieth–century interior design, however, metals have finally come into their own. These sophisticated and beautiful materials offer interior designers exciting creative possibilities, in a variety of forms and looks. It is important to note that metal's manufacture and installation require extensive experience in working, forming, finishing, and handling. This chapter should serve as the basis for a designer's further research and consultation with manufacturers and installers about specific metals, their finishes, and their most attractive and practical uses.

There are a select group of metals that are commonly used as interior finishes: steel, aluminum, stainless steel, brass or bronze, copper, and a few other varieties. If used properly, the color associated with each of these metals can serve to beautifully enhance an interior design program.

Within its working parameters, each metal can be manufactured for interior applications by using several methods, each of which offers designers a host of creative opportunities: Metals can be rolled into sheets of various thicknesses, rolled and formed into bars or rods, or cast into a variety of shapes and designs. Metals can also be finished in several surface textures. Although the terminology in some cases is the same as that used for stone, there are some important differences.

Polished. Although it is the most susceptible to scratches and other superficial damage, this rich, mirrorlike surface is the most popular metal finish. The surface of the metal is highly reflective, which also enhances its color.

Brushed. As its name implies, the surface of the metal is lightly brushed to leave regular, unidirectional scratches in either a linear or circular pattern. While it reflects less light and is somewhat less extravagant than a polished finish, a brushed finish can withstand a reasonable amount of abuse and still be attractive. Brushed finishes are commonly used in heavily trafficked areas such as elevator cars.

Matte. For this finish, the surface of the metal is polished until it is smooth but not glossy or shiny. The metal reflects light in a somewhat diffused manner and its color will look darker.

Textured. Several techniques are used to texture metals, including machining, engraving, hammering, punching, sandblasting, and etching, each of which produces several finish effects. All of these techniques can be used in conjunction with relieving, a process that abrades the raised portions of the texture.

Colored. The natural color of metals can be altered by using a variety of techniques, including applying chemicals, heat, vapors, and sawdust, to produce patination, bronzed effects, single colors, and bimetallics.

Plating. By using an electrochemical process, a very thin coating of one type of metal is applied to another. This technique can provide a base metal with the look of a more expensive metal while maintaining its desirable physical properties, such as economy, strength, or flexibility.

IN THIS UPSCALE FAST-FOOD STORE, THE CUSTOM-BUILT SERVICE COUNTERS ARE ACCENTED WITH DECORATIVE BRASS HANDRAILS. THE PAINTED STEEL-BEAM CEILING TREATMENT, WHICH REVEALS NEUTRALLY PAINTED CEILING SYSTEMS ABOVE, HELPS TO PROMOTE THE FEELING OF AN OPEN SPACE. *ALAN SCHINDLER; COURTESY OF DORF ASSOCIATES*

FLOORS

While most metals are both strong and light, they are not normally used to finish floors. Because they can be scratched and dented fairly easily, and because they are subject to greater expansion and contraction due to temperature changes than most other materials, it is difficult to install and maintain metal flooring.

Metals do fill a flooring niche as accents. Small metal tiles, which are usually about 6 inches square or smaller, are used in conjunction with stone or ceramic tiles. Metal can also be used as a linear trim. Referred to as *terrazzo strips* because they are used in terrazzo flooring (see Chapter 3, "Stone"), these bronze or zinc strips are used in the joints of stone or ceramic tile flooring and lend a formal but subtle brass or chrome accent to an installation. Their small widths, which range from 1/8 to 3/16 inch, hide most of the abuse that the metal receives from floor traffic and regular maintenance, keeping it bright and new-looking while making the surface of the joints level with the rest of the floor.

Terrazzo strips are installed in a manner similar to that used for ceramic or stone tiles, and are simply placed in the grouting space between them. The strips are tacked onto the floor with small nails or adhesive by a continuous metal piece that is attached to the back of each strip, which holds them in place until the floor is grouted. The strips can be placed in the grouting joints in a variety of configurations. Recently, a few companies have developed strips made specifically for stone or ceramic tiles that are somewhat easier to install.

Terrazzo strips can also be used to create an inset or border of carpet in a stone or ceramic tile installation. In this instance, terrazzo strips that are used at the edges of the tiles create a contour that physically divides the two materials and reinforces the edge of the installation.

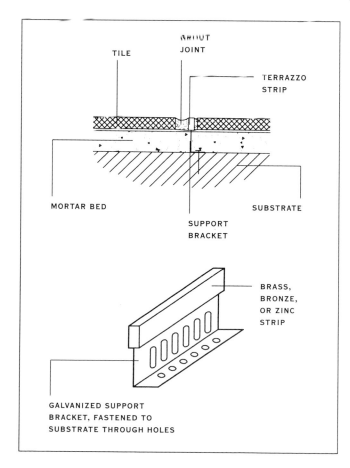

A HIGHLY DECORATIVE TERRAZZO AND STONE COMMERCIAL LOBBY INSTALLATION.

(TOP LEFT) A CROSS SECTION DRAWING OF A TERRAZZO STRIP INSTALLATION. THE STRIP IS EITHER THE FIRST OR SECOND ELEMENT IN THE INSTALLATON SEQUENCE (EITHER BEFORE OR AFTER THE MORTAR BED IS ESTABLISHED), AND IS INSERTED INTO THE GROUT JOINT BETWEEN THE TILES AND MADE FLUSH WITH THE TILE SURFACE. *(BOTTOM LEFT)* AS A FLOORING ELEMENT, METAL IS USUALLY MOST APPROPRIATE WHEN USED AS AN ACCENT, WHICH MINIMIZES THE AMOUNT OF SCRATCHING AND OTHER TRAFFIC-RELATED DAMAGE THAT USUALLY OCCURS.

As a wall finish, metal is primarily used in two forms: as paneling and as trim. When used as paneling, metal is similar to wood both in format and in manner of installation. Metal panels are either fabricated by a manufacturer in standard sizes or custom-made to account for the limitations of the material itself and the restrictions of its fabrication. The panels are rolled in large machines into flat sheets and can be made in a variety of widths. It is important to note that, primarily as a reaction to heat and cold, smaller-gauge panels of fairly large dimensions tend to bulge or buckle slightly in the middle. In most flat pieces of metal, this tendency—which is referred to as *oilcanning*—can be quite unsightly. To avoid this problem, the panels must be limited in their proportions, either in size or thickness or both. Most manufacturers limit the sizes of their panels to those that are within appropriate tolerances while still maintaining an economical thickness. Certain manufacturers have developed production techniques that allow for larger panel sizes while avoiding the problem of oilcanning. These involve sandwiching a synthetic material that is similar to plastic between two thin sheets of metal, which helps to prevent the uneven conduction of heat and cold and thereby gives the designer the benefits of both a flat surface and a very thin sheet.

Panel edges are also an important consideration. For instance, if the edges of the panels butt together to form a tight joint, there will be no room to allow for the metal to expand, which may damage the joints or cause the panels to bow. Common solutions are to use a reveal or metal trim to hide the joint. If a reveal is used, it must be wide enough to accommodate any expansion movement; otherwise, if the reveal is too small, the client will have a reveal when the panels are relatively cold, but will be forced to accept a butt joint when the panels are warm.

Because metal paneling is not commonly used as a interior finish material, designers must work with materials that are most likely intended for use as exterior cladding. This is not usually a problem, except that the installation details—most of which are designed to withstand the adverse weather conditions that would confront an exterior—may seem somewhat overdesigned for interior use.

As an accent or trim, metal is almost always mated with another material. One common use is as a divider between sections of wood paneling. While these accents can be installed flush with the panel, raised, or recessed, they are almost always used flat, as other configurations can be costly to make and install because of the specialized tools and labor involved.

Although the specific details for installation vary from job to job, there are a few areas that an interior designer should keep in mind when specifying metals. For a job of any appreciable size, the designer must first determine—possibly on the advice of a structural engineer—whether the substructure can in fact support the weight of the panels. Unless the design specifically dictates otherwise, the substructure should be level and square. Finally, as for most other finishes, the designer should rely on an experienced installer in order to avoid potential problems.

Uses for metal as a ceiling finish are discussed in depth in Chapter 11, "Ceiling Materials and Finishes." These include metal ceiling panels, ceiling grids, and linear panel strips, among others. Also, many wall configurations, which blend easily with other materials, can also be used on ceilings.

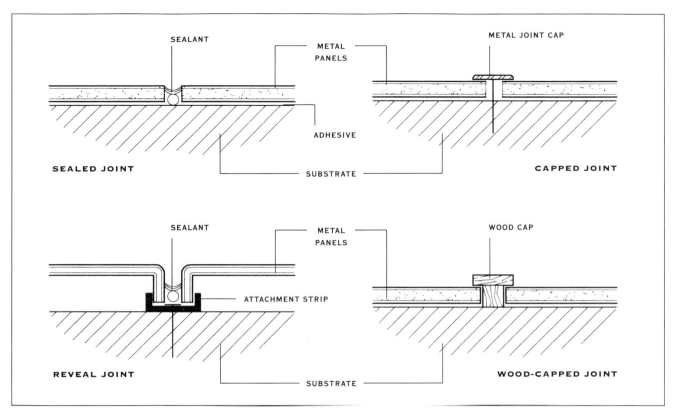

AN ASSORTMENT OF METAL PANEL JOINTS: SEALED, CAPPED, REVEAL, AND WOOD CAPPED.

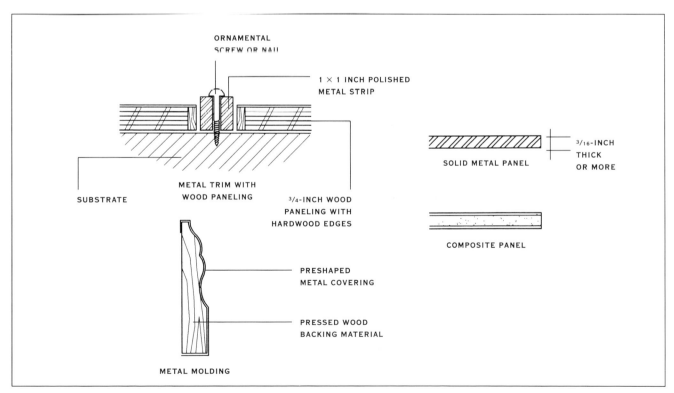

(LEFT) METAL CAN ALSO BE USED AS AN ACCENT OR TRIM, EITHER BETWEEN WALL PANELS AS STRIPS, OR AS A PREFORMED MOLDING FOR COLUMNS OR TRIM. (RIGHT) IN ORDER TO PREVENT OILCANNING, MOST MANUFACTURERS LIMIT THE DIMENSIONS OF THEIR SOLID METAL PANELS, IN SIZE, THICKNESS, OR BOTH. OTHER MANUFACTURERS HAVE SOLVED THIS PROBLEM USING A TECHNIQUE IN WHICH A SYNTHETIC MATERIAL IS SANDWICHED BETWEEN TWO THIN SHEETS OF METAL.

6

CERAMIC

AND

QUARRY TILE

BY NO MEANS MADE EXCLUSIVELY FOR BATHROOM AND KITCHEN USE, CERAMIC AND QUARRY TILE PROVIDE CONTRACT INTERIOR DESIGNERS WITH STRIKING AND ELEGANT DESIGN SOLUTIONS, PARTICULARLY IN HIGH-TRAFFIC, HIGH-VISIBILITY AREAS. *PHOTO CONTRIBUTED BY FLORIDA TILE INDUSTRIES, INC.*

Archaeological evidence indicates that ceramics were first developed in the Nile Valley approximately 2,000 to 3,000 years ago. When the step pyramid of King Zoser (c. 2600 B.C.) was excavated in 1803, glazed blue-green ceramic tiles were found intact within the burial chamber—probably the first time tiles had been used to ornament an interior space—a testament to their durability as a finish material. These early ceramic tiles were made almost exclusively in a square format and fired with bright glazes. As history has consistently shown to be the case for most other finish materials, decorative tile first graced the interiors of only the wealthy and powerful.

Later, developments in fabrication reduced the size of tiles to control the consistency and evenness of their edges and backs. The Romans decorated the interiors of their homes with marble *tessarae*, which are small pieces of colored stone, marble, or glass, although their palette was somewhat limited by the material. Within the traditions and aesthetics of Byzantine art, the early Christians adorned the interiors of their basilicas with elaborate mosaics of glass tessarae. During the Renaissance, the Dutch—and, later, the English—excelled in producing Delft tiles, which featured domestic and pastoral scenes in rich hues of blue with white. By the 1800s, manufacturing techniques could accommodate the volume production of ceramic tiles in consistent colors and sizes.

TYPES
OF TILE

Today, ceramic and quarry tiles are used in a variety of interior applications and manufactured in a wide range of colors, sizes, and textures. When an interior design program requires a finish of strength and durability, tile is often the material of choice, as it imparts a quality of permanence to a project. Most tile is composed of a blend of clay, shale, flint, and other natural materials that are extruded or pressed into various shapes and then fired in a kiln for a specified period of time. The physical characteristics of tile are important because they determine not only how a tile will look but how it will perform. There are three basic tile types: glazed ceramic tile, unglazed ceramic tile, and quarry tile, which is usually unglazed. The category of specialty tile serves as a catchall for those tiles whose differences, for whatever reason, place them outside of the primary classifications.

GLAZED CERAMIC TILE

For many people, the phrase "glazed tile" immediately calls to mind the standard 4^1/$_4$-inch square tile that can be found in most residential bathrooms. While it is probably the most common, it is by no means the only size or type available. Glazed ceramic tiles are composed of two parts: the *bisque* or the body of the tile, and the *glaze* or its surface finish. The bisque is a nonvitreous extruded or pressed clay base with a water absorption rate of 18 percent or lower. *Cottoforte* or red clay, *majolica* or yellow clay, and white clay may all be used in its manufacture. In spite of the clays' colorful names, the color of the bisque itself is neutral, providing a consistent base for any glazes that will follow.

The glaze is sprayed or painted onto the surface of the unfired bisque, which, when fired in the kiln, creates an impervious finish. Many glazed tiles are coated in a two-step process: The first glaze, which is opaque, gives the tile its color and/or texture; the second is a transparent or crystalline glaze that is applied over the first to give the surface of the tile its bright, glossy shine and to protect it against staining. The tile is fired between the application of each layer, and any further designs are applied over the second layer of fired glaze. The first glaze contains certain glass-forming minerals and pigments that yield the intended color and texture to the surface of the tile upon firing. Depending on the desired effect, the results of the second glaze can range from high gloss to matte. Some glazes are specially formulated for slip resistance or to have a somewhat abrasive finish texture.

An installation of unglazed bisque tiles would be too soft to withstand normal wear and highly susceptible to stains and dirt. The color and durability of a glazed tile, therefore, are integrally related to the strength of its fired surface. While the standard glazed tile is designed to reasonably resist abrasion when its installation is limited to vertical surfaces as well as lightly used horizontal surfaces such as some countertops, it is not designed to withstand excessive impact, nor will it perform well when subject to extremes of heat and cold. The designer should also be aware that the glaze reduces the surface's friction coefficient, thereby decreasing the tile's slip resistance, particularly when wet.

Usually about ^{5}/$_{16}$ inch thick, common glazed tile sizes are 4^1/$_4$ inches square, 4^1/$_4$ × 6 inches, and 6 inches square. Depending on the manufacturer, designers may be able to specify other sizes, including 12 inches square and larger. The term *mosaic* is used to refer to ceramic tiles (either glazed or unglazed) that are less than 6 inches square; the most common mosaic sizes are 1 inch square, 1 × 2 inches, and 2 inches square. The smallest sizes are usually used for murals or other detailed decorative patterns. Ceramic tiles that are 6 inches square or larger (up to 12 × 12 or even 12 × 24 inches) are called *pavers*.

UNGLAZED CERAMIC TILE

An unglazed ceramic tile, which is sometimes called a *vitreous tile* because of the glasslike quality of its finished surface, is not an unfired tile. On the contrary, it is fired with the same precision as a glazed tile, but at a higher temperature. Unglazed tiles are made by the *dust-pressed* or *plastic method* with clays that yield a harder, denser body than is required for a standard glazed tile, with a consistent color and composition throughout. Unglazed ceramic tiles are classified as either impervious or vitreous (see "Quality Standards," below) with a water absorption rate range of 0.5 to 3 percent, which give unglazed tile superior wearability. They are most commonly used for flooring, and are sometimes run up a wall to form a wainscot.

Unglazed ceramic tiles are generally thinner than glazed tiles (usually about ¹/₄ inch), although the thickness usually increases as the tile's facial dimensions increase. As with glazed ceramic tile, the term "mosaic" refers to tiles that are less than 6 inches square. Tiles that are 6 inches square or larger are called pavers (as are glazed ceramic tiles) or *porcelain tiles*, which again refers to the tile's mineral composition, which results in a very dense glasslike quality after firing. The smaller sizes are normally manufactured backed with paper, flexible spacers, or a mesh to facilitate proper installation. Despite the lack of colored glazing, unglazed ceramic tile colors range from light to dark and include a wide variety of light-and-dark speckled or mottled designs, all in a matte finish.

With the range of colors and shapes available, a number of interesting and appealing combinations of mosaics can be created and attached to backing for easy installation. This cuts down considerably on the labor that positioning each piece of tile within a pattern requires, as had been the practice many years ago. Today, if a designer specifies unusual patterns or custom graphics, most manufacturers can create special configurations attached to backing for an additional fee, or for a nominal charge when a minimum amount of tile is specified.

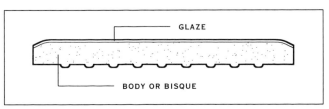

A TYPICAL 4¹/₂-INCH-SQUARE GLAZED CERAMIC TILE *(TOP)* AND A CROSS-SECTION DRAWING SHOWING THE BODY OR BISQUE AND THE GLAZE *(BOTTOM)*.

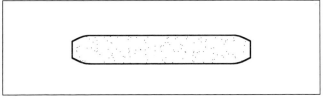

FOUR 2-INCH-SQUARE UNGLAZED CERAMIC TILES (ALSO REFERRED TO AS UNGLAZED CERAMIC MOSAICS) BACKED WITH SILICONE DISKS TO FACILITATE INSTALLATION *(TOP)* AND A CROSS-SECTION DRAWING SHOWING THE PRESSED BODY, WHOSE COLOR AND COMPOSITION ARE CONSISTENT THROUGHOUT *(BOTTOM)*.

QUARRY TILE

The strength, hardness, and moisture absorption of quarry tile are similar to those of brick because both are mixtures of similar raw materials that are then subject to comparable methods of kiln firing. While most people usually think of the 6 × 6 inch rust-red tile as the typical quarry tile, this category actually includes a wide variety of products. In technical terms, a quarry tile is a glazed or unglazed modular form manufactured from extruded shale, clay, and other earthen materials with a thickness between $1/2$ and $3/4$ inch and a facial area that exceeds 6 square inches. This allows for much latitude in the finished look of the tile, with the texture being either rough or quite smooth. All quarry tiles are characterized by a water-absorption rate of less than 5 percent.

While they are stain-resistant rather than stainproof, quarry tiles are highly resistant to moisture, oils, chemicals, and other potentially problematic materials, making them a good choice for extremely high-traffic areas such as commercial kitchens as well as a variety of exterior uses. Quarry tiles are manufactured in a range of hardnesses; a protective sealant is sometimes applied to the softer products before use, or occasionally salt-glazed before the first firing.

Quarry tile is also similar to brick in its range of available colors, which, like brick, depend on composition and length of firing time. Many quarry tiles are made in the red to brown range, but yellows and grays are also available. Slip-resistant quarry tile is created by embossing a texture onto the surface, and by mixing an abrasive aggregate into the body before firing. These tiles are especially popular in commercial situations where water and grease are common hazards.

In addition to its composition, quarry tile is similar to brick in terms of the materials and procedures used for setting. Quarry tile is usually set in and grouted with standard brick mortar, and finished with $3/8$-inch-wide joints. (See also "Setting Materials" and "Installation," later in this chapter.)

Because of the wide variety of quarry tile products available from manufacturers, designers should obtain specific information on each product to ensure that the best possible material has been specified for the intended use.

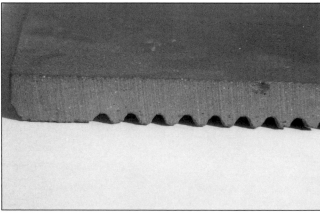

A TYPICAL 6-INCH-SQUARE QUARRY TILE SHOWING THE TEXTURE OF THE KILN-FIRED SURFACE *(LEFT)* AND THE TILE EDGE *(ABOVE)*.

SPECIALTY TILE

The three categories discussed above include the majority of tiles used today. However, there are still many tiles that vary from these categories in one way or another, due to differences in overall facial size, thickness, color or texture, method or color of glaze, shape, or recommended method of installation. They also may have important technical characteristics relating to impact-resistance, slip-resistance, and resistance to frost, chemicals (both natural and manmade), staining, and so forth. Tiles that fall into one of these special categories are chosen by a designer to satisfy a particular need or intended use, although in many cases the initial choice is based on appearance because the performance characteristics of the tile are already established by virtue of its special category. The designer then studies the published data on the product or meets with the manufacturer's representative to determine whether the tile has any limitations. At that point, the initial choice is either changed or confirmed. When choosing tile from one of the three basic categories outlined above, the selection is made because the program requires specific performance characteristics, such as those exhibited by quarry tile, with the colors or textures then chosen from within that particular group. While both methods of selection are valid and both design and performance are important, the designer should make a tile's performance characteristics his or her primary consideration.

Because imported ceramic tiles make up a significant portion of the tile market in the United States today, designers should be especially aware that while the quality standards of many imported tiles either equal or surpass those set by the U.S. tile industry, much of the test data for these tiles conform to foreign standards. It is advisable, therefore, for designers to obtain confirmation from the manufacturer in writing that an imported products' standards comply with U.S. requirements, unless the tile will be used exclusively for decorative purposes. When choosing tile for a project, a designer must determine whether an imported tile is essential to the integrity of the design program and so should be specified by trade name, or whether portions of the specifications should be modified to give other manufacturers, either domestic or foreign, an opportunity to submit fair and competitive bids. This means that he or she may need to do some investigative work in order to become adequately informed about a particular imported tile.

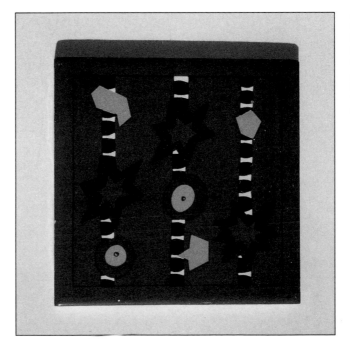

A SPECIALTY GLAZED CERAMIC TILE WHOSE HIGHLY UNUSUAL CONTEMPORARY GRAPHIC WAS APPLIED TO ITS SURFACE FOLLOWING THE SECOND FIRING OF GLAZE.

While reviewing the various tile types above, basic quality standards or requirements that govern the manufacture of ceramic tile, such as size, porosity, and hardness, are cited. The industry standards for tile are published by the American National Standards Institute (ANSI). The standard governing ceramic tile, A137.1-1980, specifies that a tile judged as "standard grade" is harmonious in color, free from any facial imperfections that are visible at a distance of three feet, and devoid of structural defects. This means that standard-grade tiles have passed tests governing breaking strength, abrasion resistance, and bonding strength.

In addition to this model, there is a "seconds" classification that is identical to the requirements of the standard grade with the exception that imperfections may not be visible at a distance of 10 feet, as well as a Special Purpose classification that covers specialty tiles.

POROSITY

Regardless of composition and number of glazes, all tiles will absorb a certain amount of water. The degree of absorption relates to a tile's strength and durability. Each of the following terms is assigned a corresponding range of water absorption rate that defines a tile's porosity: *Nonvitreous tile* has a water absorption rate of more than 7 percent; *semivitreous tile* has a water absorption rate of between 3 and 7 percent; *vitreous tile* has a water absorption rate of between 0.5 and 3 percent; and *impervious tile* has a water absorption rate of 0.5 percent or less. In general, the higher the porosity, the softer the tile; the lower the porosity, the greater a tile's strength and hardness.

TILE POROSITY DESIGNATIONS	
DESCRIPTION	**CORRESPONDING WATER ABSORPTION RATE**
NONVITREOUS	7–18 PERCENT
SEMIVITREOUS	3–7 PERCENT
VITREOUS	0.5–3 PERCENT
IMPERVIOUS	0.5 PERCENT OR LESS

HARDNESS

The quality or characteristic of hardness is actually a function of the manufacturer's specifications rather than a governmental requirement. Certain standards of hardness are used consistently throughout the industry, so that a manufacturer would recommend a particular tile for an intended use depending on both the hardness of the glaze and the strength of the body.

SIZE

Sizes are normally given as *nominal dimensions*, which are close approximate measurements that are used solely for informational purposes. This is done simply because it is easier to specify a 2 × 2 inch tile instead of a $1^{15}/_{16} \times 1^{15}/_{16}$ inch tile. When exact sizes are critical to the design of a project, they must be cited in the specifications.

COMMON TILE SIZES AND TRIMS				
	GLAZED CERAMIC (IN INCHES)	UNGLAZED CERAMIC (IN INCHES)	QUARRY (IN INCHES)	PAVER (IN INCHES)
STANDARD SIZES	2 × 6	3/4 × 3/4	3 × 3	2 × 8
	4 1/4 × 4 1/4	1 × 1	4 × 4	6 × 6
	6 × 6	1 × 2	6 × 6	8 × 8
		2 × 2	8 × 8	12 × 12
		1-INCH HEXAGONAL	12 × 12	
		2-INCH HEXAGONAL	HEXAGONALS AND OCTAGONALS IN VARIOUS SIZES	
SPECIAL SHAPES	BEADS	BEADS	BULLNOSES	BULLNOSES
	BULLNOSES	BULLNOSES	COVED BASES	CAPS
	COUNTER TRIMS	COVES	INSIDE AND OUTSIDE CORNERS	COUNTER TRIMS
	COVED BASES	INSIDE AND OUTSIDE CORNERS		INSIDE AND OUTSIDE CORNERS
	CURBS	SWIMMING POOL NOSING		
	PARALLELOGRAMS			
	TRIANGLES			

NOTE: AS SIZES AND SHAPES VARY AMONG MANUFACTURERS, DESIGNERS SHOULD CHECK WITH INDIVIDUAL SUPPLIERS FOR THE EXACT DIMENSIONS OF THEIR PRODUCTS.

While the size of a specific tile does not affect its quality or strength, it is absolutely essential that, when specifying tile, designers inquire about and confirm a specific tile's available dimensions, as not all tiles are made in all sizes. He or she should indicate exactly which sizes are needed and verify that they are indeed available in the desired pattern. These points are especially important when two or three alternative products will be reviewed when a project is bid on.

SLIP RESISTANCE

Since tile is often used as a flooring material, its resistance to slippage is of the utmost importance. Determining just how slippery a given tile can be for a specific intended use is quite difficult: Tiles are more slippery when wet than when dry, and when walked on with certain types of shoe soles. Given the litigious temperament of our society, manufacturers are reluctant to associate specific guidelines or recommendations with their products because they could be held accountable for an accident even when conditions are beyond their control.

ANSI defines a slip-resistant tile as one "having greater slip resistance characteristics due to an abrasive admixture, abrasive particles in the surface, grooves or patterns in the surface, or a glaze specifically designed for increased coefficient of friction." While informative, this statement is still very general. The standard, therefore, is determined to a great extent by what the designer decides will best fit specific needs regarding slip resistance. Designers should evaluate what constitutes a slip-resistant tile on a project-by-project basis.

SETTING
MATERIALS

There are two basic elements that are used to set or install tile: mortar or adhesive and grout. Mortar is used to attach the tile to the substrate, and, in some cases, stabilize it. Adhesive is used in the same manner as standard mortar, but its composition makes it more convenient to use. Grout is used to fill in the spaces between each piece of tile. It is important to note that any tile is only as good as its installation, and that setting materials are an integral and decisive part of that process.

MORTARS AND ADHESIVES

Next to the tile itself, the mortar is the most important element in creating a finished tile surface. It is used to adhere or attach the tile to the surface on which it is installed, and provides it with a *setting bed*, which is the underlying surface that supports the installation and holds the tile in place. Ideally, the mortar should hold the tile firmly, resisting motion in any direction. If mortar is not installed properly, the tile will not perform as it should.

Setting beds are classified into two general categories: *thick-set installation* and *thin-set application*. Until fairly recently, thick-set installation was the most common method. The tile is set into a *mortar bed*, which is a layer of cement-based mortar, about $1^1/4$-inches thick for floors and $^3/4$-inch thick for walls. Because of the thickness of the mortar, this type of setting bed resists movement, provides a good base for the installation, and enables the installer to slope the floor to a drain if necessary. Thick-set tile can also accommodate space to reinforce the setting bed, which is sometimes necessary when the subfloor is not as rigid as the specifications require. In this case, a metal lath or wire mesh specifically manufactured for this purpose is installed.

Thin-set application, on the other hand, essentially involves installing tile with a thin layer of a mortar that is more like an adhesive or a glue, usually about $^3/32$- to $^1/8$-inch thick. Its main advantage is that the designer does not have to allow for the overall thickness of the tile and the setting bed at adjoining surfaces. Before their formulations were improved, thin-set mortars were not strong enough to stabilize the installation when the floor moved and, in many cases, did not provide adequate bonding strength between the tile and the mortar and/or the mortar and the substrate. This caused tiles to crack under only moderate pressure or impact, or to pop loose from the mortar due to movement. With the thin-set mortars available today, these kinds of problems have been virtually eliminated.

A CROSS-SECTION DRAWING SHOWING THE BASIC ELEMENTS OF A TILE INSTALLATION: THE TILE, THE SETTING BED, AND THE GROUT.

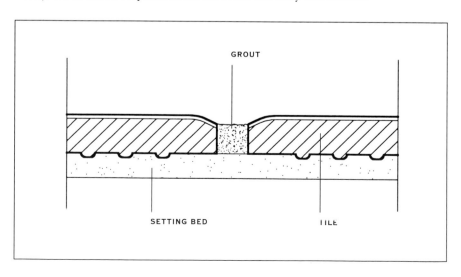

GROUT

SETTING BED

TILE

There are six general types of mortar, each of which is designed to fill a specific purpose: portland cement mortar, dry-set mortar, latex portland cement mortar, epoxy mortar, modified epoxy emulsion mortar, and furan mortar. While the traditional cement-based mortars (portland, dry-set, and latex portland) do not yield the performance results of the non-cement-based mortars (epoxy, modified epoxy, and furan), the latter are, in general, significantly more expensive. Designers should ask their installers to inform them of the costs involved with each product and its installation to prevent any misunderstandings.

Portland cement mortar. This type of mortar, which is typically used in thick-set installations, is similar to brick mortar in its basic composition. Depending on its use, the proportions of sand, portland cement, and water of a mixture will vary. For walls, the standard mortar mixture is 6 parts sand and 1 part portland cement with water; for floors, the mixture includes lime, and the proportions of sand, portland cement, and lime with water range from 5:1:$\frac{1}{2}$ to 7:1:1. Installation involves spreading the mortar onto the substrate to a specified thickness. This mortar is especially useful when sloping a drainable floor or reinforcing a setting bed, and provides a stable surface on which to install the tile. Tiles can be set into a bed composed of this mortar when it is still plastic or "wet," or installed with another mortar or adhesive over the portland cement mortar once it has cured. When installing tiles with a high absorption rate over wet mortar, they must be soaked in water beforehand to prevent them from absorbing any of the mortar's moisture, which is essential for proper curing and bonding.

Dry-set mortar. This mortar, which is a mixture of portland cement, sand, and special additives that improve its ability to retain water, is most commonly used in thin-set applications. (In fact, in some locations the terms "thin-set" and "dry-set" are used interchangeably.) The additives also increase its bonding strength, particularly when used as an adhesive. This mortar is designed to be used in a one-layer process and can be spread as thin as $\frac{3}{32}$ inch. Because of its water-retentive characteristics, it does not require that the tile be soaked prior to laying. If any leveling or draining of the floor surface is necessary, a setting bed must be installed first. For most thin-set applications, however, dry-set mortar is a good choice.

Latex portland cement mortar. Similar to dry-set mortar in its application and installation, the distinguishing ingredient of latex portland cement mortar is a latex-based additive that makes it less rigid than dry-set mortar while maintaining excellent bonding strength. This product's primary disadvantage is that it must be allowed to dry completely when used in high-moisture areas such as sinks, showers, and pools, which can take as long as 36 to 48 hours.

Epoxy mortar. This mortar is formulated specifically for use where resistance to chemicals is an issue. Epoxy mortar is composed of epoxy resins and hardeners, which form a base with a very high bonding strength as well as high impact-resistance.

Modified epoxy emulsion mortar. A modified epoxy mortar is something of a hybrid, combining the characteristics of standard epoxy mortar and dry-set mortar. The addition of portland cement and sand to epoxy resins and hardeners results in an economical mortar with high bonding strength and little or no shrinkage during curing. This product requires a very stable substrate, and must be spread to cover the laying surface completely.

Furan mortar. This product is designed to be installed in settings where resistance to chemicals is a consideration, such as commercial testing laboratories. Furan mortar can be installed over concrete, wood, plywood, steel plate, and even ceramic tile.

Adhesives compose the second category of mortar-related setting materials. A tile-setting adhesive is basically a very thick glue that is thinly spread over the surface of the setting bed and then scraped and evenly distributed with a notched trowel. Most adhesives do not require mixing or the addition of other materials, which makes them extremely convenient to use. In addition, at the end of the day or when a job is completed, the remainder of the adhesive can be saved and used again.

There are two types of tile-setting adhesive. *Organic adhesive*, the most common, has the consistency of a thick, very sticky glue. It is recommended for interior use only, and cannot be used to level or *true up* a surface. *Epoxy adhesive* is similar to organic adhesive except that it contains epoxy resins and hardeners, which give it increased bonding strength.

All mortars and adhesives accomplish the same task: to attach tile to the substrate. To ensure that what he or she has specified is in fact appropriate for a particular job, a designer should consult the manufacturer's published data, the manufacturer's representative, and a professional tile setter.

GROUT

Grout is applied to the joints between tiles to complete the tile surface. It binds the tiles to one another and eliminates most of the space between the joints where water, dirt, and other debris might accumulate. Although it is quite similar to mortar in composition, its consistency is smoother so that it will fill the spaces between the tiles more efficiently. There are six basic grout types: portland cement grout, sand portland cement grout, dry-set grout, latex portland cement grout, mastic-type grout, and silicone rubber grout.

Portland cement grout. Formulated from portland cement and other materials and mixed to yield a dense, water-resistant product, portland cement grout is used primarily with floor tiles, as it has a similar water-absorption rate.

Sand portland cement grout. The most commonly used grout for both ceramic and quarry tiles, this mixture of portland cement and sand (which is usually mixed on the job) may be used with either wall or floor tiles.

Dry-set grout. Special additives enable this portland cement–based grout to retain its own moisture during curing, thus lessening the extent to which the tile must be soaked before installation, depending on the additives present in the particular product. It is suitable for use in both wall and floor installations.

Latex portland cement grout. This is any one of the above grouts combined with a latex additive that enhances its cohesive, adhesive, and water-retentive properties. While a variety of latex materials can be added to the grout, acrylic resin has the lowest water absorption rate and is the most resistant to ultraviolet radiation and to yellowing over time, which helps to preserve any coloring agents that may have been added to the grout. This product's one disadvantage is that it tends to leave a film on the face of the tile that must be removed. If tended to promptly, it can be removed with little effort; however, the longer the film remains on the tile, the more difficult its removal becomes.

Special grout materials. There are a few other grouts made for specific purposes. *Mastic-type grout*, which is similar to organic adhesive and available in a ready-to-use form, is not normally intended for use in high-traffic areas. *Silicone rubber grout* is a preformulated rubberlike sealant that bonds to tile immediately. It is most commonly used with pregrouted tiles, where some grouting is still required for installation. It resists staining, shrinking, cracking, and moisture, and is more expensive than standard grouts.

INSTALLATION

The proper installation of any tile product is one of the fundamental prerequisites of its long and successful life. Even when the designer has chosen a tile that is appropriate for its intended use, and whose color, size, and pattern are consistent with the design program, faulty installation procedures alone can ruin this part of a project. When each of its elements is carefully prepared or selected to meet the needs of the particular site, a tile installation should last for many years.

Most tile is installed in the same general way, which involves a fairly simple set of procedures. First, the substrate is prepared for the setting bed and/or the installation of the mortar. The installer then places the tiles on this surface, making certain that they are level and uniformly spaced. The grout is applied by spreading it onto the tile surface and forcing it into the joints repeatedly to ensure full and dense penetration. The excess grout is removed and the tile is allowed to cure or dry. If experience indicates that the grout will be difficult to remove, it is applied directly to the joints to minimize contact with the tile surface, making cleanup considerably easier.

In a successful installation, the tile, the mortar, the grout, and the quality of their installation are interdependent and act as a single unit. Unfortunately, there are several factors that make each element difficult for a designer to control. First, the condition and/or preparation of the substrate will greatly affect the final installation. Second, there are probably as many manufacturer-recommended installation procedures as there are types of tile. Third, each installer is likely to have his or her own way of doing the job. With all these considerations, it is essential that designers educate themselves or consult knowledgeable sources before specifying tile.

There are two basic areas that a designer should be conscious of when specifying or overseeing the installation of tile. First, make certain that the substrate has been properly prepared, which is somewhat easier to do in a new installation. This means that the surface should be clean, durable, and dimensionally stable. The importance of meticulousness cannot be overemphasized. The substrate should be free from dust, sand, and any foreign materials left behind from other work, such as drywall mud, paint, or stain, all of which can wreak havoc with the installation, as can waxy or oily films or residue from curing compounds. If especially dirty or messy work is due to take place beforehand, the designer would be wise to specify that the substrate be covered with a plastic or canvas tarp to protect the surface and ensure that any and all materials that might hinder the bonding of the tile to the substrate will be avoided. For existing surfaces, the designer must determine the stability and strength of the substrate: Old concrete may be cracked or brittle, and plywood subfloors might not be suitable for tile. The tile manufacturer's sales representative can prove to be a valuable source for suggestions when such problems arise: A thick-set installation might work; a new layer of plywood subfloor might be another solution; an epoxy mortar and grout system might be a third. But the end result should be the same: a surface stable enough to provide a good base for the installation of tile.

A designer should also carefully consider the intended use of the finished tile surface when specifying installation materials. For an area that will be subject to a great deal of water or moisture, such as a shower or pool area, a waterproof membrane should be specified. In a lab or other setting where caustic chemicals are used, grouts and mortars of an appropriate type should be specified. If the possibility of staining exists, a sealer would be appropriate. If a considerably large area of tile is desired, the designer should plan in expansion joints in consultation with the tile manufacturer. Finally, a designer should make note of when and how the tile makes contact with other finish materials, and consider some design solutions.

CARE AND MAINTENANCE

The care and maintenance of tile actually begins in the early stages of the project, when the designer chooses tile appropriate to the intended use of a space and specifies and implements the proper installation procedures. In addition to these preliminary considerations, the manufacturer's recommended maintenance procedures should also be followed. In most cases, the care and maintenance of ceramic tile is relatively simple. However, both the designer and the client—especially since the latter is usually involved in this stage of the tile installation—should remember that tile is not indestructible. The following example serves to illustrate a common maintenance problem.

An indoor swimming pool and adjoining locker room were specified with 1 × 1 inch ceramic tile. Claiming that their experience had shown that an initial coat of sealer would make the tile much easier to maintain, the client's maintenance crew applied a sealer that was not recommended by the tile manufacturer. After a few months, the floor began to look noticeably dingy and dirty, and repeated attempts to clean it were unsuccessful. The problem was blamed on faulty tile. After the designer and the tile representative investigated the matter, they discovered that a sealer had been used, and that several coats of a shiny wax had also been applied. The sealer and wax had reacted with the moisture and the chlorine in the water to create a mildewlike substance within each coat of wax, which discolored the sealer and caused the tile to look dull and dirty. The tile representative recommended that the client remove the wax and sealer in order to restore the tile to its original look. This succeeded to a great degree, but the grout was left looking dingy and gray. Unfortunately, the client was then forced to live with the consequences of the maintenance crew's decision or consider having the tile completely regrouted.

Designers should inform their clients about the general care and maintenance procedures recommended by both the manufacturers of the tile and setting materials. If any problems occur, the manufacturers are then obligated to correct them.

GENERAL GUIDELINES FOR TILE CARE AND MAINTENANCE		
TYPE OF TILE/USE	ROUTINE CLEANING	HEAVY-DUTY CLEANING
GLAZED TILE WALLS, COUNTERTOPS	WIPE WITH A DAMP CLOTH OR SPONGE USING AN ALL-PURPOSE CLEANER. USE A WINDOW CLEANER FOR GLOSSY SURFACES. WIPE DRY WITH A CLOTH.	CLEAN WITH SCOURING POWDER, A COMMERCIAL TILE CLEANER, OR AN ALL-PURPOSE CLEANER USING A NONMETALLIC SCOURING PAD OR A VERY FINE-GRADE STAINLESS-STEEL PAD. RINSE AND WIPE DRY.
GLAZED TILE FLOORS	VACUUM REGULARLY TO REMOVE GRITTY PARTICLES. DAMP MOP WITH A SOLUTION OF WATER AND "SOAPLESS" DETERGENT.	USE A COMMERCIAL TILE CLEANER OR A STRONG SOLUTION OF WATER AND "SOAPLESS" DETERGENT. IF STAINED, USE SCOURING POWDER PASTE. LET STAND FOR FIVE MINUTES, THEN BRUSH AND SCRUB. RINSE AND LET DRY. FOR LARGE OR PROBLEMATIC AREAS, A POWER SCRUBBER IS RECOMMENDED.
UNGLAZED TILE WALLS	SPONGE WITH A DILUTED SOLUTION OF WATER AND "SOAPLESS" DETERGENT.	USE SCOURING POWDER PASTE. LET STAND FOR FIVE MINUTES, THEN SCOUR WITH A BRUSH. RINSE AND WIPE DRY.
UNGLAZED TILE FLOORS	VACUUM REGULARLY TO REMOVE GRITTY PARTICLES. DAMP MOP OR SPONGE WITH WATER AND/OR A DILUTED SOLUTION OF WATER AND "SOAPLESS" DETERGENT.	USE SCOURING POWDER PASTE. LET STAND FOR FIVE MINUTES, THEN SCOUR WITH A BRUSH. RINSE AND WIPE DRY. A SMALL BRUSH IS SUITABLE FOR SMALL FLOORS; A SCRUBBING MACHINE IS RECOMMENDED FOR LARGER AREAS.
SOURCE: CONTRIBUTED BY FLORIDA TILE INDUSTRIES, INC.		

CERAMIC AND QUARRY TILE ARE PARTICULARLY POPULAR AS A FINISH IN RESTAURANTS AND OTHER FOODSERVICE ESTABLISHMENTS. A SELECTION OF POSSIBLE APPLICATIONS *(CLOCKWISE FROM TOP LEFT, THIS PAGE):* A CORPORATE CAFETERIA, A FAMILY-STYLE EATERY, A CASUAL PUB, AND A FUN 1950s THEME LUNCHROOM FOR A SMALL BUSINESS.

7

RESILIENT

FLOORING

RESILIENT FLOORING IS ONE OF THE MOST VERSATILE FLOORING SOLUTIONS USED IN CONTRACT INTERIORS. IN THIS SPACE, TILES IN SINGLE PRIMARY COLORS ARE USED AS A BORDER AND INTERSPERSED WITH COMPLEMENTING SPECKLED TILES. *PHOTO BY THE MAKERS OF ARMSTRONG RESILIENT FLOORING*

One of the three types of interior floor coverings, resilient flooring includes those products whose general characteristics fall somewhere between hard and soft floor coverings. *Hard floor coverings* are hard, unyielding surfaces such as brick, ceramic or quarry tile, stone, and wood. *Soft floor coverings* are characterized by tufted or woven surfaces, such as carpet, rugs, mats, and so forth. As the name suggests, most resilient floor coverings will deform to a load to some degree, then return to their original shape when the load is removed.

Although the ancient Egyptians used an asphalt-based flooring material, resilient flooring as we know it today was developed fairly recently, in the early 1800s. At that time, resilient flooring consisted simply of heavy fabrics such as canvas that were oiled or waxed, giving homeowners an inexpensive way to cover a dirt or stone floor. Experiments with various mixtures did not begin until the mid-1800s, when mass-production techniques were first applied to resilient flooring manufacturing.

A composite flooring material composed of rubber, sawdust, and cork was invented in 1840. In 1860, a mixture of linseed oil, wood flour, cork dust, and pigments, which came to be known as *linoleum*, was developed. When exposed to and mixed with air, linseed oil takes on a rubbery consistency, and when blended with other materials and a variety of gums or resins, it formed a resilient, durable material. The linoleum mixture was then pressed into thin sheets, which gave it a glossy surface. These sheets were then glued onto a felt or burlap backing and coated with wax or lacquer. A pattern could be pressed into the surface for an inlaid design.

While its development was a major milestone in history of the resilient flooring industry, linoleum had some major drawbacks. Because it had a tendency to degrade in the presence of moisture, it was recommended for use only above grade, where it could be kept dry. Also, linoleum stained easily, primarily as a result of its organic composition.

During the 1950s, the flooring industry first responded to linoleum's limitations with the introduction of *asphalt tile*, which was basically composed of limestone and asbestos fillers and asphaltic binders, with pigments added for color. This mixture formed a durable, stable product that was comparatively inexpensive. Due to asphalt's characteristic dark color, the color range of asphalt tile was limited to only dark tones. (It was later discovered that similar properties could be obtained with coal tar and petroleum-based resins, which made lighter colors possible.) Asphalt tile was primarily manufactured in 9-inch-square tiles, simply because the fillers in its composition were not flexible enough to allow it to be made into sheet goods.

As one of the least expensive types of resilient flooring—also requiring the least maintenance—asphalt tile became extremely popular. Like the linoleum that had inspired its invention, asphalt tile had several flaws, all of which were a result of its oil-based composition: Its resistance to staining by grease and oil was quite poor, it was easily damaged by oil-based solvents and animal fats, and its brittle structure did not resist denting well.

Today, linoleum and asphalt tile have for all practical purposes disappeared from the U.S. flooring market. Their shortcomings—as well as various shortages caused by World War II—motivated the technical innovations that led to the development of plastic and vinyl flooring. The current group of offerings from resilient flooring manufacturers has stabilized into a few general classifications, although there is no single formula for the fabrication of flooring in any one classification. In view of the intensely competitive market, manufacturers will continue to incorporate further advances in synthetic materials into their product lines as they occur.

ONCE THE UNDISPUTED LEADER OF THE RESILIENT FLOORING MARKET, LINOLEUM WAS EXTREMELY POPULAR BOTH RESIDENTIALLY AND COMMERCIALLY. THE EMBOSSED LINOLEUM SHOWN AT LEFT WAS FIRST RELEASED IN 1962. *PHOTO BY THE MAKERS OF ARMSTRONG RESILIENT FLOORING*

MATERIALS

Today, there are two primary materials that are commonly used in the manufacture of resilient flooring: vinyl and rubber. Because cork and trowel-on flooring occupy a relatively small share of the resilient flooring market, the properties of their materials are discussed under "Types of Resilient Flooring," later in this chapter.

A derivative of polyvinylchloride (PVC), vinyl is used in the majority of resilient flooring produced today. It is a durable, plasticlike material that, when combined with other materials, can take on a variety of characteristics, many of which are both relevant and appropriate to resilient flooring. Vinyl can be mixed with large amounts of fillers, which impart desirable properties to the finished product. A very durable substance, vinyl is not affected to any great degree by continuous contact with water, and resists the adverse affects of many acids and solvents.

Most vinyls used in resilient flooring today are composed of five elements: resins, stabilizers, plasticizers, fillers, and pigments. While each of these elements is contained in nearly all vinyl flooring products, the exact formulations vary from product to product, and particularly among manufacturers. These proprietary formulas represent much research and development and are therefore carefully guarded.

Resins give the main part of the flooring surface strength and resistance to abrasion. Stabilizers reinforce the flooring during the manufacturing process and after its installation. Although the addition of plasticizers may seem unnecessary given vinyl's inherent flexibility, they help to retain the vinyl's resiliency after it has been mixed with the other flooring components and after installation, as it ages. Because more than a "reasonable thickness" in the *wear layer*, which is the uppermost portion of the flooring, is not cost effective for the manufacturer, its finished thickness is, in almost every case, too thin to endure the traffic, weight of furniture, and other abuses without tearing and stretching. Fillers, therefore, are added to give flooring dimensional stability, thickness, and bulk, and to increase its flame-spread rating by reducing smoke generated during a fire. Limestone is the most common bulk filler used, although clay and talc are also prevalent; mineral fillers are added for their fire-resistant properties. Lastly, pigments remove the transparent look that most pure vinyls have while adding color.

Rubber's resiliency, durability, and stability make it virtually ideal for resilient flooring, and for the most part it performs extremely well in that capacity. Like most other flooring materials, however, it does have its limitations: It damages easily when exposed to petroleum solvents and oils, and its color range is confined to mostly dark colors.

Rubber was first used as a flooring material in the 1920s. Relatively easy to manufacture and install, it was used in situations where linoleum and asphalt tile were not suitable. When vinyl-based products were first introduced, rubber flooring lost most of the market it had gained. After its look was improved and its range of available colors was extended, the same basic product made something of a comeback in the 1960s.

Rubber flooring today is primarily composed of styrene butadiene, a synthetic rubber product. As with most other resilient flooring products, rubber flooring is a blend of many materials that each impart a specific characteristic to the finished product: resins as hardeners, for strength; hydrocarbon oils as extenders; minerals as fillers; and sulfur and zinc oxide as vulcanizing agents.

TYPES OF RESILIENT FLOORING

Formulated to meet the needs of a variety of commercial and residential situations, there are four major types of resilient flooring manufactured today: vinyl, rubber, cork, and trowel-on.

VINYL COMPOSITION TILE (VCT)

While searching for ways to improve asphalt tile, vinyl was first incorporated into existing asphalt products and found to be an excellent binder with many desirable properties. Eventually, asphalt was entirely replaced by vinyl, resulting in *vinyl-asbestos tile*, which became the most commonly used commercial resilient flooring since the 1950s. When the hazardous properties of asbestos were revealed, it was replaced with other fillers, creating *vinyl composition tile*, or VCT, which is still in use today and considered the standard resilient flooring finish for virtually any setting. It is routinely used in large areas in food and department stores, schools, hospitals, and other commercial spaces. It is the most economical of all resilient flooring products and, if installed and maintained properly, will perform well for many years.

The composition of VCT is about 80 percent fillers and 10 to 12 percent vinyl resins, with the remaining balance being stabilizers and plasticizers. These materials are combined in large industrial mixers that are used to prepare a somewhat doughlike compound. This mixture is then passed through a number of calendaring machines to form long patterned sheets in uniform thicknesses ($^{1}/_{8}$ inch is most common, although $^{3}/_{32}$ inch is also produced). A heated glossy finish is then applied to the surface of the sheet. After cooling, it is cut into 12×12 inch tiles and packaged.

The identifying characteristic of VCT is its "grain," which is actually composed of colored particles or chips in varying sizes and shapes. The color and configuration of the grain can be subtle, or may differ from the background dramatically. Regardless of its arrangement, the grain is consistent from face to back so that, over time, the wear pattern will not be clearly evident.

VCT is available in a variety of colors and patterns, including those that simulate brick pavers, ceramic tile, and wood parquets. It is also manufactured in accent strips, about $^{1}/_{2}$ to 2 inches wide, typically in solid colors. A recently introduced product incorporates abrasive particles into the tile, for situations where slip resistance is a consideration.

VCT normally has a load limit of around 75 psi, which is quite satisfactory for most general uses. With a relatively high percentage of fillers, it is not as resilient as some products. The key to its satisfactory performance is its maintenance. Following installation, it should be given several coats of a good wax and heavily buffed, which will fill the surface pores and provide an additional wear layer of sorts.

THIS CHART INDICATES THE PERCENTAGE OF EACH COMPONENT OF VCT: FILLERS, 80 PERCENT; VINYL RESINS, 10 TO 12 PERCENT; PLASTICIZERS AND STABILIZERS, 5 PERCENT OR LESS.

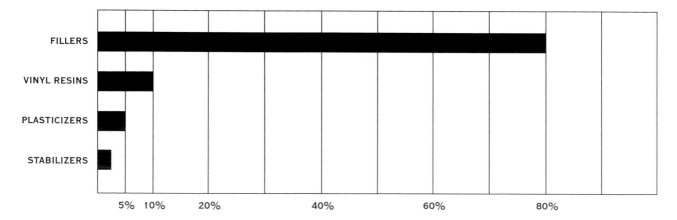

FILLERS

VINYL RESINS

PLASTICIZERS

STABILIZERS

5% 10%   20%   40%   60%   80%

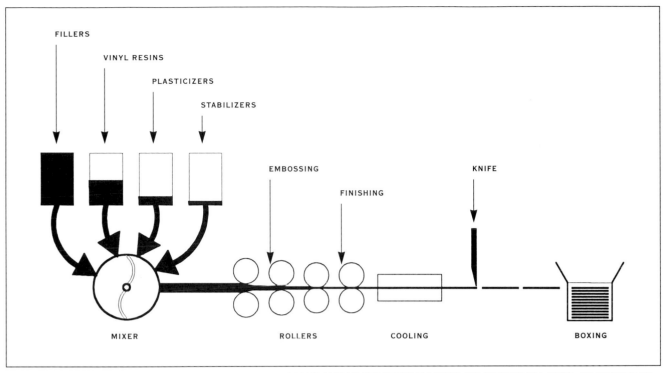

FILLERS

VINYL RESINS

PLASTICIZERS

STABILIZERS

EMBOSSING

FINISHING

KNIFE

MIXER

ROLLERS

COOLING

BOXING

A GRAPHIC REPRESENTATION OF THE MANUFACTURE OF VCT: THE BASIC COMPONENTS OF THE FLOORING ARE BLENDED IN A MIXER, CALENDARED TO FORM LONG PATTERNED OR EMBOSSED SHEETS, THEN FINISHED WITH A GLOSSY SURFACE. THE SHEETS ARE COOLED, CUT INTO 12 × 12 INCH TILES, AND BOXED FOR FUTURE USE.

VINYL COMPOSITION TILE, OR VCT, IS A HIGHLY ADAPTABLE FORM OF VINYL FLOORING. *(LEFT)* PAIRED WITH CONTRASTING ACCENT STRIPS AND SMALL LIGHT-COLORED SQUARES, WHITE VCT MAKES AN ELEGANT PRESENTATION IN A HOTEL LOBBY. *(RIGHT)* VCT CAN ALSO BE MANUFACTURED TO SATISFY MORE FUNCTIONAL NEEDS, SUCH AS THIS SLIP-RESISTANT PRODUCT, IN WHOSE COMPOSITION ABRASIVE PARTICLES HAVE BEEN INCORPORATED. *PHOTOS BY THE MAKERS OF ARMSTRONG RESILIENT FLOORING*

VINYL TILE

Vinyl tile is considered to be a grade above VCT, with increased resilience and flexibility. This is a result of a decrease of fillers in its composition (to about 65 percent). The increase in vinyl resins (to about 25 percent) makes it possible to mold the material more easily, and enables it to render color—and imitate other finishes, such as stone or wood—more accurately than VCT. While vinyl tile's patterns, colors, and general look are quite similar to VCT's—including its tile and accent strip dimensions—it simply has more of vinyl's desirable characteristics.

Vinyl tile has several other measurable advantages over VCT. Vinyl tile has a higher compressive capacity, and will support around 125 psi—about 75 percent more than VCT. It has a much higher resistance to abrasive wear and will withstand impact loads much better, and is also more resistant to cigarette burns.

Among its disadvantages, vinyl tile is considerably more expensive than VCT, though this is normally offset by its benefits. It is manufactured in much the same way as VCT.

A CHART INDICATING THE PERCENTAGE OF EACH COMPONENT OF VINYL TILE: FILLERS, ABOUT 65 PERCENT; VINYL RESINS, ABOUT 25 PERCENT; PLASTICIZERS, UNDER 10 PERCENT; STABILIZERS, UNDER 5 PERCENT.

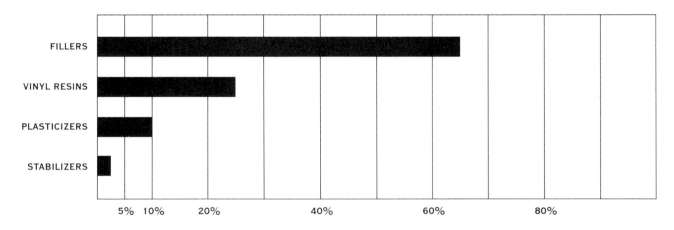

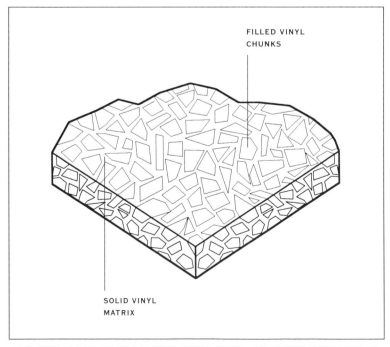

MOST SIMILAR TO VINYL TILE IN COMPOSITION, FILLED AND BACKED SHEET VINYL IS COMPOSED OF VINYL-BLEND CHIPS THAT ARE AFFIXED TO A BACKING AND SUSPENDED IN A PURE VINYL MATRIX.

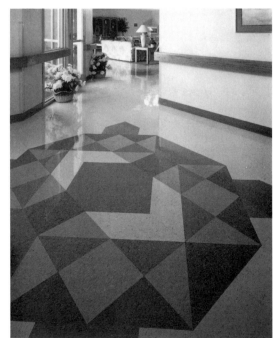

VINYL TILE IS PARTICULARLY APPROPRIATE FOR HIGH-TRAFFIC AREAS. *PHOTO BY THE MAKERS OF ARMSTRONG RESILIENT FLOORING*

SHEET VINYL

Sheet vinyl products are manufactured in a wide range of configurations to fit many different needs. Basically, sheet vinyl flooring is fabricated from vinyl materials, and produced and classified as filled or unfilled, either with or without a backing and/or a cushion.

FILLED AND BACKED SHEET VINYL

The vinyl sheet flooring product most similar to vinyl tile in composition is *filled and backed sheet vinyl,* which, while it is manufactured on a backing, it is not a completely filled vinyl. The filled portion of the sheet, which is manufactured in a manner similar to that used for vinyl tile, is broken down into small pieces called *chips.* Chips of various colors and sizes are used to create many pattern combinations. These chips are affixed to the backing, and a pure vinyl material is then poured into the spaces between them. The pure vinyl adds wearability while the chips impart stability and mass, resulting in a very resilient wear layer with a pleasing random appearance. By varying the thickness of the wear layer, the wearability of the product can be closely manipulated. Manufacturers are able to control the cost of production—and, in turn, the retail prices for its target markets—by fabricating wear layers that will not exceed their intended period of use.

The felt backing material to which the wear layer is attached serves two primary functions. By helping to stabilize the material, the percentage of fillers necessary to reinforce the wear layer is thereby reduced, which in turn increases the flooring's flexibility. In addition, in many instances the thickness of the wear layer required for adequate wearability is substantially less than that required for stability, so that the presence of backing also reduces the necessary thickness of the wear layer. You can determine whether a particular flooring product has a backing material by simply examining a sample: When looking at its edge, backed vinyl sheet flooring usually has two distinct layers of material, and the back of the sample is white or gray and much softer than the face.

Federal standards govern the required thicknesses of sheet vinyl materials for a variety of intended uses. Most commercial sheet vinyls have a wear layer of about 0.05 inch, with an overall thickness of about 0.08 inch. They are manufactured in 6-foot widths and lengths of up to 90 feet.

SOLID SHEET VINYL

This vinyl flooring product is referred to as "solid" because the wear layer *is* the entire product. This particular combination of vinyl, stabilizers, plasticizers, and fillers is formulated to function without a backing. Designed primarily for heavy-duty use, solid vinyl flooring is manufactured in a manner similar to that used for backed sheet vinyl, except that it contains more plasticizers and less fillers, which increases its flexibility. This augments the product's resilience, which in turn increases its resistance to abrasion, wear, and chemicals.

Solid sheet vinyl has two disadvantages. Because of the high percentage of vinyl in its composition, solid sheet vinyl is comparatively expensive, and therefore is usually used only when extremely high traffic will justify the additional cost. Also, since it does not have a backing, a flat, smooth, dry substrate is imperative to this product's installation.

While solid sheet vinyl is most commonly produced in 6-foot widths, widths as narrow as 4 feet and as wide as 6¹/₂ feet are also available. The standard thickness is 0.08 inch, but 0.06 inch is not uncommon.

CUSHIONED SHEET VINYL

This product is used almost exclusively by the residential market. It does, however, have some commercial applications.

Cushioned sheet vinyl is composed of four distinct layers that work together to provide certain desirable characteristics. The bottom layer is usually a felted backing; in some cases, a highly flexible vinyl is used. In either case, it provides a stable material to which the next layer, the *cushion*, is attached. The cushion is a liquid plasticizer that is applied to the backing with a liquid blowing agent that changes to a gas when subjected to heat. This heated mixture of plasticizer and blowing agent then expands to produce the bubbles or voids that in turn create the cushion. The application of heat simultaneously fuses the cushion to the backing and gelatinizes and smooths out its surface to prepare it for the next layer. This dense cushion is designed to give the product more resilience than other sheet vinyls and extend its resistence to extreme impact and wear.

The third layer of cushioned sheet vinyl is the flooring pattern. In most resilient flooring products, the pattern extends beneath the surface of the wear layer, with the pattern created by chips that have been applied to the backing, which can be time-consuming and costly and may require specialized machinery. In cushioned vinyl products, the visible pattern or design is printed and/or embossed onto the gelled surface of the cushion layer by means of a printing process known as *rotogravure*, which gives the product a realistic look that is nearly impossible to achieve through stamping or pressing. Limited only by the dimensions of the printing drum, the printed image can consist of one or many colors, a design of any complexity or scale, or a photographic reproduction of another finish material such as ceramic tile or brick. (In the latter case, the designer should keep in mind that, regardless of the quality of the printed image, the vinyl flooring still presents only a graphic representation of the actual material. Aesthetic considerations may then overshadow this material's possible cost savings or relative ease of installation.) The fourth layer is the wear layer, which is a clear protective coating made of plastisol or pure clear vinyl that is specially formulated to resist wear and abrasion. Upon completed assembly, the entire composite is heated to a specified temperature for a specific period of time, which completes the formation of the cushion layer and fuses all the layers together.

CUSHIONED SHEET VINYL IS COMPOSED OF FOUR LAYERS: A FELTED OR HIGHLY FLEXIBLE VINYL BACKING; A CUSHION LAYER THAT IS CREATED FROM HEATED LIQUID PLASTICIZER; THE PATTERN, PRINTED BY ROTOGRAVURE; AND A CLEAR PLASTISOL OR PURE VINYL WEAR LAYER.

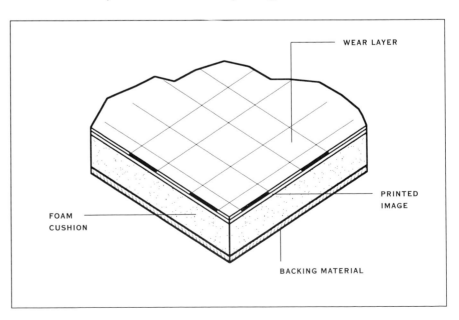

WEAR LAYER

FOAM CUSHION

PRINTED IMAGE

BACKING MATERIAL

Because it is extremely flexible and lightweight, cushioned sheet vinyl is normally made in 12-foot widths, although the thickness will depend on the product and/or the manufacturer. In any event, the overall thickness of this type of vinyl flooring has no bearing on its durability, which instead is determined by the thickness of its wear layer. Generally, the minimum wear layer thickness of cushioned vinyl flooring ranges from 0.010 inch (for inexpensive, light-gauge flooring) to 0.020 inch (for commercial and more costly residential flooring).

In addition to its increased resilience and resistance to wear, cushioned vinyl flooring has two advantages, both a result of the presence of the cushion: First, the flooring feels more comfortable underfoot; second, the cushion helps to reduce impact noise between floors. When compared with other types of resilient flooring, its greatest disadvantage is its tendency to tear or puncture when objects are moved on it, which is a result of the combination of the wear layer thickness and load resistance of the cushion. However, this only means that reasonable care should be taken when such a situation arises.

RUBBER TILE AND SHEET GOODS

Rubber flooring has several favorable characteristics. Simply by virtue of its basic component, it has exceptional resistance to wear and abrasion. It is also resistant to cigarette burns, which is an important consideration for public sites where smoking is permitted. While rubber flooring stains easily when exposed to hydrocarbons and vegetable oils, it is highly resistant to many chemicals and solvents such as acetone and esters. As mentioned above, among its limitations are its restricted color palette (light, bright colors are difficult to produce in this type of flooring) and its relatively high cost.

THE EMBOSSED PATTERN OF RAISED DOTS IS A TYPICAL FINISH OF RUBBER TILE AND SHEET GOODS. THESE PRODUCTS ARE MOST APPROPRIATE IN AREAS WHERE EXPOSURE TO EROSIVE CHEMICALS IS A CONSIDERATION. *PHOTO BY THE MAKERS OF ARMSTRONG RESILIENT FLOORING*

The manufacture of rubber flooring begins with the blending of its various components in a mixer. The flooring compound is then rolled and formed into a roughly final shape and size in a special four-roller press. During this process, the material may be embossed with either the raised dot or square patterns that are characteristic of much of today's rubber flooring. At this point, the material is either cut into pieces and stacked (for tile) or fed through another type of press and rolled (for sheeting). In either case, the product is pressed at high heat for approximately 10 minutes, then aged for a few days before it is cut and trimmed to its final size.

Rubber tiles are commonly cut into 9-inch and 12-inch-square sizes, with larger sizes such as 18 × 36 inches and 36 square inches also available. Sheet goods are usually available in roll lengths of about 35 inches, from 36 to 48 inches wide. Both products are made in $1/8$-inch and $1/16$-inch thicknesses. Note that, for European manufacturers, these sizes are only approximate metric conversions.

Patterns in rubber flooring are fairly limited to simple designs: raised discs, squares, and linear ribs, as well as a smooth surface. While the most common colors are solid, many manufacturers produce multicolor designs similar to those in VCT products, usually on the smooth-textured rubber products. Most rubber flooring products come from the factory with a low-to medium-gloss whose maintenance normally only requires buffing. Some manufacturers will apply a sealer to the surface to help maintain the shine and minimize staining problems.

OTHER RESILIENT FLOORING MATERIALS

There are two other resilient flooring products that, while not nearly as common as vinyl or rubber products, still fill specific needs: cork tile and trowel-on flooring.

Cork tile is, as its name suggests, fabricated from cork, a product of wood bark. The tile itself is made from small cork particles that have been mixed with a resilient binder, and is pressed under heat and pressure into its final thickness. This process also compresses the wear layer, making it more durable. A plastic or resinous coating may be added to improve its wearability as well as add a shine.

THE BASIC COMPOSITION OF CORK TILE: SMALL PARTICLES OF CORK SUSPENDED IN A RESIN-BASED FILLER, HEATED AND COMPRESSED TO A DURABLE THICKNESS. A PLASTIC OR RESINOUS COATING MAY BE ADDED TO PROVIDE A GLOSSY FINISH AND ENHANCE WEARABILITY.

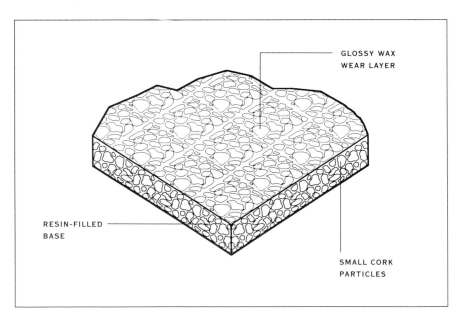

GLOSSY WAX WEAR LAYER

RESIN-FILLED BASE

SMALL CORK PARTICLES

IN ADDITION TO
RESIDENTIAL
INTERIORS, CORK
TILE IS SUITABLE
FOR LOW-TRAFFIC
COMMERCIAL
USE. *PHOTO BY
THE MAKERS
OF ARMSTRONG
RESILIENT
FLOORING*

Cork tiles are both resilient and sound absorbent. After a surge of initial popularity in the 1950s, cork tile's benefits were achieved somewhat more easily and inexpensively by some of the newer vinyl products. Cork tile's main disadvantages are a direct result of its primary component: It absorbs moisture and stains easily, and since cork is itself not a strong material, its use is limited to low-traffic areas. The best method of maintaining a cork tile floor is with frequent, heavy coats of wax, which will help to limit the cork's rate of wear.

Trowel-on flooring is more common than cork tile floors but is used primarily in special locations. This extremely durable product enables the installer to control the thickness of the floor (within specified parameters, of course), and to extend the surface up the wall to form a heavy base. In certain situations, such as a commercial kitchen where there are many pieces of equipment with curbs or many drains, and when cost is a factor, this type of flooring is a good choice. It is available in a variety of colors and textures. Note that if the subfloor is subject to high levels of moisture, this product's weakest point is the joint between the floor and the base.

INSTALLATION

The process of installing resilient flooring consists of a generally simple set of procedures. As with other finish materials, the manufacturer's recommended procedures should be followed to ensure proper installation.

Planning. Once the installer has measured the dimensions of a space and examined its configuration, he or she will then plan how and where to start. If tiles are being installed, the installer will start in the center of the room to ensure that any cut or trimmed tiles will be equal in size around its perimeter. With sheet flooring, he or she will plan where the seams in the floor will fall. The designer should resolve with the installer any concerns about a particular job before any work begins.

Preparation. Preparing the subfloor beforehand is probably the most important step in the installation process. The subfloor must be swept or mopped to remove all dirt, dust, and other debris so that the adhesive and the flooring will bond completely. Cracks or other defects in the subfloor should be repaired, as they will eventually damage or show through the resilient flooring. Small cracks can be filled with a floor putty such as Florestone. If a crack is large or actively spreading, more serious steps should be taken to remedy the situation.

Mastic. After the subfloor has been prepared and its surface is clean and dry, the adhesive or mastic is applied with a notched trowel to a small area. This area, which should be specified by the mastic manufacturer, is related to how much tile or flooring can be laid before the mastic *sets up* or dries. The flooring is then laid onto the floor. Again, tile is installed starting at the center of the room and working toward the walls, normally in quarters. Any space around the perimeter of the room that is less than a tile wide must be cut to fit. For sheet goods, the product is placed in its intended position. Half of the cut sheet is rolled back onto itself and the adhesive is applied to the exposed area of the floor. The sheet is then rolled back onto the adhesive and smoothed out. The other half is folded back and the process is repeated.

The completed installation is then rolled with a heavy hand roller to securely set the tiles or sheets into the adhesive, level the floor, and eliminate any air bubbles or pockets of surplus adhesive that might create bumps or cause problems later.

A SELECTION OF TOOLS AND MATERIALS USED TO INSTALL RESILIENT FLOORING *(CLOCKWISE FROM TOP):* A NOTCHED TROWEL; A SCRIBER, WHICH IS USED TO MARK SEAMS WITH A SCRATCH BEFORE THEY ARE CUT; A SMALL CONTAINER OF ADHESIVE; A LINOLEUM KNIFE; A STRAIGHT-EDGE, WHICH IS USED TO CUT SEAMS; AND A SEAM ROLLER.

CUTTING AND
SEALING A SEAM
IN VINYL SHEET
FLOORING. *PHOTOS
BY THE MAKERS
OF ARMSTRONG
RESILIENT FLOORING*

There are several products related to resilient flooring that serve as transitory materials between finishes or building elements. They include bases, transition strips, and stair treads.

The *base* forms the bottom of the wall and covers the joint between the wall and floor with a horizontal element that gives the room an attractive, finished look. Available in three heights—2½, 4, and 6 inches—resilient flooring bases are made of either vinyl or rubber in three basic styles. The most common, the *top-set* or *coved toe base*, has edges that are tapered to fit snugly against the surfaces of the flooring material and the wall. It is installed with mastic and a notched trowel, after the flooring has been laid. A similar configuration is known as the *butt-cove base*. Instead of being tapered, its toe ends in a flat edge that will butt against the edge of any ⅛-inch-thick resilient flooring. This type of base must be installed before the flooring material; additional care must be taken to ensure that the edge of the base is straight. The third type is called a *carpet base*, which is installed with its straight, square toe on top of the carpeting, creating a smooth transition by slipping down into the pile.

To reduce the number of joints, resilient flooring bases are usually manufactured in 4-foot lengths or long rolls. There are inside and outside corners available, but with today's more flexible products, they bend quite satisfactorily around an outside corner. Careful cutting can also ensure good inside corners. But the designer should investigate both to see which method is most desirable.

When choosing a base, some interior designers, architects, and builders prefer rubber to vinyl, arguing that rubber is more stable and will not shrink or change color over time. This is no longer the case. Recent technological developments have put vinyl and rubber on the same level, though vinyl still offers a wider range of colors. Note, however, that some vinyl manufacturers use a high percentage of fillers, which makes their base products less flexible and more susceptible to shrinking. This can be especially problematic at corners, as substandard vinyls will look lighter at bends where the material stretches, creating an unattractive weak point that could tear after repeated impact. Unless you are willing to spend time investigating a product, it is best to work with a reputable manufacturer.

THE THREE
STANDARD TYPES
OF RESILIENT
FLOORING BASES:
BUTT-COVE, TOP-
SET, AND CARPET.

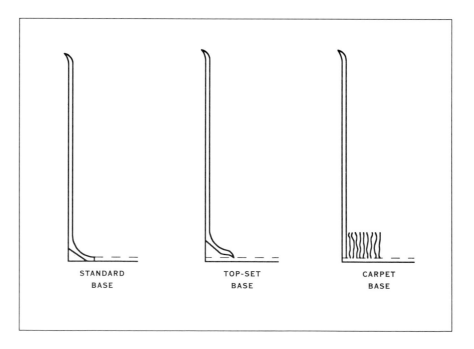

STANDARD
BASE

TOP-SET
BASE

CARPET
BASE

While they are not produced by as many manufacturers as bases, *transition strips* are an important resilient flooring accessory. Available in a wide range of thicknesses, they create a transition between materials of different heights or textures. Thin strips are used between VCT and concrete; thicker strips are used between VCT and carpet or tile. Transition strips are available in basically the same colors as bases, and are installed in much the same manner.

Resilient flooring *stair treads* can significantly enhance the look of a set of stairs. Required by building code in all structures over one story in height, stairs that are open to offices or rooms should be finished in some way. Manufactured in a variety of textures—smooth, ribbed, dotted, and even with abrasive particles for extra slip resistance—stair treads also help to prevent slipping.

(ABOVE) HIGH-QUALITY VINYL FLOORING BASES FLEX EASILY AROUND CORNERS, AND DO NOT LOOK TENSED OR STRAINED WHEN ARCHED OR CURVED. *PHOTOS BY THE MAKERS OF ARMSTRONG RESILIENT FLOORING*
(LEFT) ALTHOUGH BOTH VINYL AND RUBBER FLOORING BASES ARE AVAILABLE IN A WIDE RANGE OF COLORS, IT IS STILL EASIER TO PRODUCE LIGHTER AND BRIGHTER TONES IN VINYL.

8

CARPETING

CARPETING CAN HELP SET THE TENOR OF ANY ROOM. IN THIS CASE, A HIGH-QUALITY INSTALLATION IMPARTS A RESIDENTIAL CHARACTER TO THIS LIVING ROOM—STYLE GATHERING AREA IN A COUNTRY CLUB LODGE. *PHOTOGRAPHY BY JON MILLER, HEDRICH-BLESSING; POWELL/KLEINSCHMIDT, INTERIOR ARCHITECTS*

As there are very few projects that do not involve its specification, carpeting has become an integral part of the contract interior design industry. Current professional terminology defines *carpeting* as a floor covering composed of heavy woven or tufted fabric that is usually, though not necessarily, installed from wall to wall.

The first carpets were probably woven grass mats used by the ancient Egyptians to cover bare dirt floors. The Assyrians and Babylonians are said to have created beautiful woven floor coverings for their royalty. Knotted carpet fragments from the Middle East, dating from 600 to 500 B.C., have been unearthed as evidence of a continuously developing craft and means of trade. Eventually, knowledge of weaving and loom work spread to Europe, where the flat-woven or tapestry weave rugs developed around A.D. 1000. As a result of the Muslim influence, carpets were woven in Spain from the early twelfth century. The French (and the Flemish who staffed their factories) were particularly accomplished weavers and textile manufacturers, and the tapestries created at Aubusson—founded in the late thirteenth century—and Gobelin—established in Paris in the fifteenth century—gained world renown. In the 1600s, the French government subsidized the development of the Savonnerie knotted pile carpets. When French weavers emigrated to England in the eighteenth century, they set up handlooms in Axminster and Wilton. These looms were mechanized 100 years later following the Industrial Revolution. Other technological advancements such as the flying shuttle (a weaving device), the spinning jenny (a spindle machine), and the jacquard weaving process (which used an apparatus that wove figured fabrics) all helped to further promote carpeting's popularity as a common floor covering.

CARPET FIBERS

Because of the physical limitations of nineteenth-century looms, carpeting was then manufactured exclusively in 27-inch widths. With the development of the tufting process in the early twentieth century, this standard width was increased. By the 1950s, the tufting method was used to manufacture carpet for the general public, and today almost all carpeting is manufactured by this process.

Regardless of the method of manufacture, most carpeting uses a variety of yarn types in its primary construction. Because they form most—if not all—of a carpet's pile, the content of the yarn is crucial. While they may be made of any fiber that is appropriate to the weaving process, almost all yarn fibers that are used in the manufacture of carpet can be classified into two categories: natural and man-made.

Natural fibers are derived directly from materials found in nature; these fibers (as they are used in carpet yarns) are wool (by far the most popular), cotton, flax, and silk. (Cotton is used for residential carpeting only, and silk, or a combination of silk and wool, is used to make Oriental rugs.) Each may require some cleaning, combing, or spinning in order to procure fiber in a usable form, but all are used without chemical additions or alterations. (Due to its hazardous properties, asbestos, a natural mineral fiber, cannot be used in products intended for interior applications.)

In contrast, *man-made fibers* are usually derived from a natural material such as petroleum or cellulose (wood fiber), but are then modified extensively to create a new substance. The resulting fibers are produced in shapes that are somewhat similar to those found in natural fibers, which enables manufacturers to use them in weaving or tufting. Because of their lower cost, generally superior appearance, improved wearability, and excellent color rendition, man-made fibers are in many cases more desirable than their natural counterparts.

The first man-made fiber was produced in 1884 from liquid cellulose that was extruded into a long threadlike fiber. The extrusion process was eventually refined and the new fiber was commercially manufactured in France under the trade name of artificial silk in 1891. This material, which came to be known as *rayon*, was finally perfected in 1929. Production for *acetate*, the second cellulose-based fiber, was begun in 1924. After a long period of research and development, *nylon* was the first fiber to be produced entirely from chemicals. It was a huge success following its introduction in 1939. Today, there are several fibers that are used in the manufacture of carpeting, both natural and man-made.

CARPET FIBERS	
NATURAL	**MAN-MADE**
WOOL	RAYON
COTTON	ACETATE
FLAX	NYLON
SILK	POLYESTER
	POLYPROPELINE (OLEFIN)
	ACRYLIC

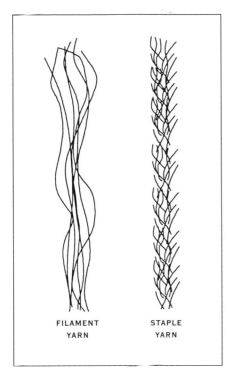

FILAMENT
YARN

STAPLE
YARN

THE TWO YARN TYPES THAT ARE USED IN
CARPET CONSTRUCTION: FILAMENT YARNS,
WHICH ARE COMPOSED OF SEVERAL LONG
TWISTED FIBERS; AND STAPLE YARNS, WHICH
ARE MADE UP OF MANY SHORT FIBERS THAT
HAVE BEEN INTERWOVEN INTO A SINGLE UNIT.

SINCE THEIR INTRODUCTION IN 1947,
MANUFACTURERS HAVE CONTINUED TO
EXPERIMENT WITH NYLON FILAMENT SHAPES
IN ORDER TO MEET THE DEMANDS OF THE
MARKET. THE "FIRST GENERATION" CIRCULAR
SHAPE TENDED TO EMPHASIZE DIRT AND
GENERATE STATIC ELECTRICITY. THE "SECOND
GENERATION" SAW THE DEVELOPMENT OF THE
TRILOBAL FIBER AND THE FOUR- OR FIVE-
SIDED HOLLOW FIBERS, WHICH HELP TO HIDE
DIRT BY DIFFUSING LIGHT. TODAY, THESE
IMPROVED SHAPES ARE TREATED WITH
ANTISTATIC AND SOIL-REPELLANT CHEMICALS.

WOOL

Used to manufacture carpets for hundreds of years, wool is still synonymous with carpeting of the highest quality. One reason for its excellent reputation is its composition. The outer portion of the wool fiber is composed of scalelike cracks that resist dirt, making maintenance easier. At the center of the fiber is a bundle of long round cells that give it strength and elasticity, which enable it to retain its appearance longer because it resists permanent damage from bending and crushing. In addition, wool has a soft feel and dyes extremely well.

Wool's main disadvantage is its cost. Initially, the price difference between wool and synthetic fibers was substantial. With the current instability of world oil prices, however, wool has become increasingly competitive.

NYLON

Nylon is the most popular fiber used to manufacture carpet today. It was used as a staple fiber when it was introduced in 1947 and became widely accepted because of its low cost and durability. Derived from petroleum and nitrogen, nylon is a carbon-based polyamide fiber. The "first generation" product was extruded through a spinncrette to create long filaments, which were then grouped together and twisted into a single continuous yarn or cut into shorter lengths and spun into staple yarns. This early product's shape, which had a round cross section, tended to magnify dirt and soil as the light passed through it. It also had a propensity to generate static electricity, creating annoying shocks.

The shape of the fiber was modified in the "second generation" of development into either a trilobal or delta shape, or a four- or five-sided shape with holes in its center. These new shapes helped to diffuse or refract the light as it passed through the fiber, which helped to hide the soil particles as they settled into the carpet.

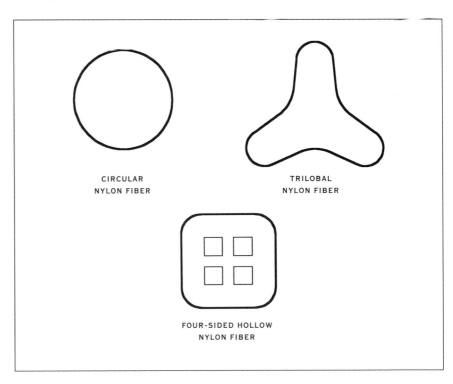

CIRCULAR
NYLON FIBER

TRILOBAL
NYLON FIBER

FOUR-SIDED HOLLOW
NYLON FIBER

The "third generation" of fibers addressed nylon's natural tendency to generate static by incorporating a carbon or metallic fiber into the yarn or by adding antistatic chemical treatments to the basic polymer. This development was particularly important in commercial interiors, where the use of static-sensitive computer equipment was on the rise.

In an effort to further improve nylon's dirt-resistant properties, the finished carpets were treated with soil-repellent chemicals. The latest improvements attempt to apply these treatments to the fiber *before* it is spun into yarn rather than after it has been woven into the carpet, which is thought to extend the fiber's soil-resistant characteristics.

POLYESTER

Polyester fibers are derived from a synthetic polymer that is composed of molecular compounds found in dehydric alcohol and terepathalic acid. These fibers are made in staple form with cross sections specifically designed to help hide soil. Known for its soft feel and bulky look, polyester had problems early on with *crushing*, which is a yarn's lack of resilience when subjected to heavy traffic. Its performance was improved when the yarns were twisted and the shape was set with heat, and the finished carpet was tufted to an appropriate density. Like nylon fibers, polyester fibers are also sometimes treated to improve dirt resistance and decrease static generation.

POLYPROPYLENE (OLEFIN)

Polypropylene fibers are based on ethylene, propylene, and other olefins. These fibers are very light, strong, and extremely resistant to chemicals. Because a finished polypropylene fiber is also quite resistant to pigment in carpet dyes, color is usually added to the molten fiber before it is extruded. This process, referred to as *solution dyeing* (discussed later in this chapter), creates colors that are extremely fade-resistant when exposed to sunlight or cleaning solvents. Polypropylene fibers are used extensively in the manufacture of indoor-outdoor carpeting and in imitation grass carpets (which are made with flat, ribbonlike yarns). They are resistant to mildew, bacteria growth, and decay.

Initially, polypropylene fibers, like polyester, also had problems with crushing. Various methods were developed which greatly improved their performance, including spinning the yarn more tightly to enhance resilience and tufting the carpet to a greater density.

ACRYLIC

First developed in the 1950s, acrylic fibers are a synthetic polymer composed primarily of acrylonitrile units. *Modacrylics*, which are acrylics blended with another material, contain less than 85 percent of acrylonitrile units in their composition. Once extremely popular, these fibers are not used as extensively as they once were. Through various methods of fiber blending, they can produce very attractive carpets in both the level loop and cut pile styles. Acrylic fiber carpets are similar to wool in feel, are fairly lightweight, and resist damage from chemicals and fading due to sunlight quite well. Colors are usually added by the solution dyeing process.

CARPET MANUFACTURING

After the fibers have been spun into yarn, the next step is the manufacturing of the carpeting itself. There are three major methods used to construct carpets today: weaving, tufting, and needlepunch. In addition, a few less widespread processes are also discussed below.

WOVEN CARPETS

Woven carpets are constructed by interweaving the *pile* or surface yarns with those that form the backing in a manner that is similar to that used to manufacture textiles. As a result, the pile yarns are quite close together, which makes carpets of this type quite suitable for high-traffic areas. There are three types of woven carpets: velvet, Wilton, and Axminster.

The simplest of the woven carpet manufacturing processes, *velvet carpet* is usually produced in solid colors, although some color and texture variations are available.

Wilton carpets are manufactured on a special loom using the jacquard technique, which uses perforated pattern cards to control the distribution of the various colored yarns into the machine. With this method, many colors can be used to reproduce designs accurately. All of the yarn is woven directly into the surface of the carpet, and a specific color of yarn is only brought through the surface of the carpet when it is needed. These hidden yarns add body, weight, and strength to the construction.

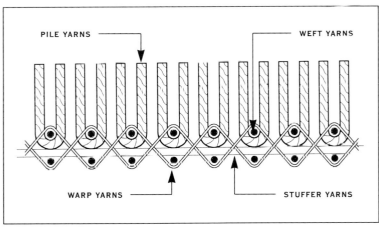

THE VELVET WEAVE IS FORMED BY LOOPING THE PILE OVER WIRES INSERTED ABOVE THE WARP.

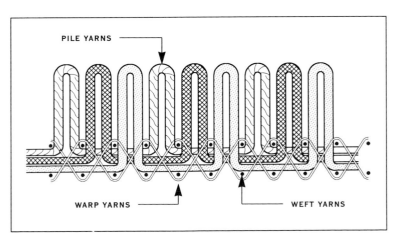

IN THE WILTON PROCESS, THE YARN IS WOVEN DIRECTLY INTO THE WARP.

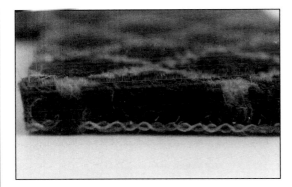

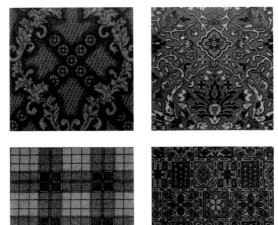

(TOP) A CROSS-SECTION VIEW OF A WILTON CARPET. THIS WEAVING PROCESS IS USED TO PRODUCE INTRICATE MULTICOLORED PATTERNS *(ABOVE)*.

OTHER MANUFACTURING PROCESSES

There are a few other types of carpeting that fill particular needs. *Needle-bonded carpeting* consists of a running layer of carpet fibers through which barbed needles are punched with a machine. After this process is repeated many times, the fibers are intertwined to create a dense mat very similar to felt, though it is thicker and has a much coarser texture. This manufacturing technique is used for some types of indoor-outdoor carpeting, as well as in products where appearance is not a primary concern.

As is implied by its name, *knitted carpeting* is actually knitted by a machine that uses one needle for each loop across the entire carpet width. The main advantage of knitted carpeting is that a greater amount of the yarn is available for wear than with tufted carpeting. This type of carpet also has several disadvantages: It has a tendency to stretch, particularly in a diagonal direction; and because of the knitting process, it is quite difficult to create a neat seam during installation.

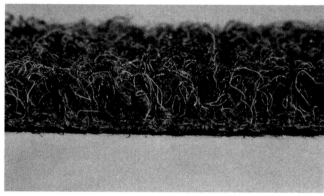

OVERVIEW *(LEFT)* AND CROSS SECTION *(ABOVE)* PHOTOGRAPHS OF A NEEDLE-BONDED CARPET.

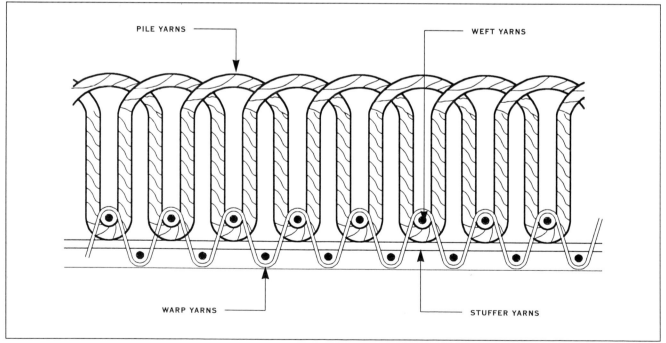

WITH NEEDLES SIMILAR TO THOSE USED FOR HAND KNITTING, THE KNITTED PROCESS LOOPS TOGETHER THE BACKING, STITCHING, AND PILE YARNS IN ONE STEP.

MODULAR CARPETING

Also referred to as *carpet tile, modular carpeting* is a fairly new development that was designed to solve some of the problems that are inherent in standard *broadloom* (which simply means that the carpet has been produced on a wide loom). This product, whose popularity is growing steadily, deserves some special attention. It is amazingly versatile and, when installed correctly, the nearly hidden tile joints create a subtle and attractive grid pattern.

As the term itself indicates, modular carpeting is similar in concept to tile flooring. In its construction, carpet tile manufacturers use techniques similar to those used for broadloom, but the final result is distinct in several important ways, with its basic configuration being the most obvious. The typical modular carpeting size is 18 inches square, although a few companies make 24-square-inch and even 36-square-inch sizes. It is critical that every tile is exactly the same size so that all of the corners align in both directions. If they do not, the installation will be severely compromised. While modular carpeting is tufted to its primary backing in much the same way as tufted broadloom, the tufts are bound to the backing by a fusion-bonding process that strongly secures the tufts and the backing together. In addition to size, the other essential difference between broadloom and modular carpeting is the latter's secondary backing, which is made from vinyl, rubber, or a similar (and sometimes proprietary) resilient material. The secondary backing is either fused or securely glued to the primary backing to produce a virtually single entity, creating the stability inherent in modular carpeting.

Carpet tiles are installed over an application of a releasable adhesive, which ensures a bond between the tile backing and the floor surface. Each unit of carpet tile itself is extremely stable and resists curling and fraying. The perimeter tiles require a continuous application of adhesive to ensure stable placement. (One manufacturer uses a heavy, semi-soft vinyl composition backing to safeguard placement.)

THE SMALLEST UNIT OF CARPETING, THE STANDARD DIMENSIONS FOR CARPET TILE ARE 18 × 18 INCHES. THE SECONDARY BACKING, WHICH IS THE OTHER DISTINGUISHING FEATURE OF MODULAR CARPETING, IS FUSED TO THE PRIMARY BACKING, PROVIDING THE TILE WITH EXCELLENT STABILITY.

CARPET SPECIFICATIONS

With the many variables that are possible in tufted and woven carpeting, the quality and specifications of the final product can vary widely. When a designer specifies carpeting for a particular project, he or she begins by attempting to answer several questions: Which type of yarn? Which construction type? How will it wear? Which color is most appropriate? When choosing carpeting or when comparing a number of carpets, a designer reviews the *specifications*, which are the manufacturer's detailed list of characteristics, of each one. Familiarizing yourself with the kinds of traits that the manufacturers cover and how they reflect the quality of the carpet will help you to determine the best choice. The specifications are usually listed on the back or underside of the display folders that contain the carpeting samples.

The following are the most important elements of a carpet's construction. Other items, such as yarn type, backing materials, and so on (covered earlier in this chapter), while not as important as those discussed below, are still quite valuable in determining a carpet's suitability.

GAUGE

Also referred to as *needles per inch*, the term *gauge* refers to the spacing, in inches, between the tufting needles across the width of the carpet. Carpets of $1/8$ or $1/10$ gauge are the most common today. *Needles per pitch* is more commonly used to describe woven carpets, with the word "pitch" referring to the number of yarn loops across a 27-inch width of carpet. Therefore, a 216-pitch carpet contains 216 loops across 27 inches, or 8 loops per inch of carpet width. All of these terms are factors in a carpet's density.

STITCHES PER INCH

As a carpet passes through the tufting machine, the needles punch tufts into the carpet backing. *Stitches per inch* refers to the number of stitches or punches the machine makes, per inch, along its length. The term *rows per inch* is also used to refer to this specification.

A DETAILED DRAWING SHOWING SOME OF THE BASIC SPECIFICATIONS OF CARPETING: GAUGE, OR NEEDLES PER INCH; STITCHES OR ROWS PER INCH; AND PILE HEIGHT.

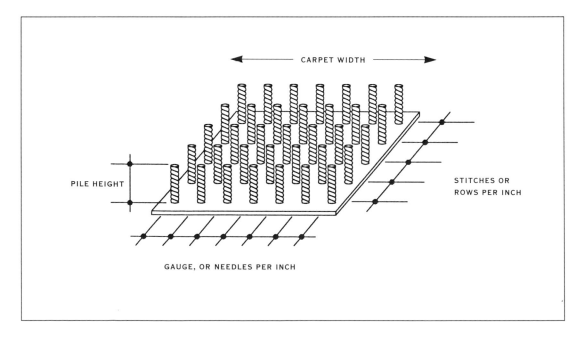

CARPET WIDTH

PILE HEIGHT

STITCHES OR ROWS PER INCH

GAUGE, OR NEEDLES PER INCH

TUFTS PER SQUARE INCH

This term refers to a carpet's density factor. The stitches per inch multiplied by the gauge or needles per inch will yield the tufts per square inch. This particular specification is quite valuable in determining how a carpet will perform: The higher the number, the greater the carpet's wearability and value (more yarn per square inch). When the tufts are very close together, dirt tends to remain on or close to the surface. The pile tends to remain upright because each tuft is supported by those around it. For instance, a $^1/_{10}$ gauge cut pile carpet with 8 stitches per inch equals 80 tufts per inch.

FACE WEIGHT

Although the specification of face weight is one of the most important considerations in evaluating a carpet, it is often mistakenly used as the sole mark of a carpet's quality. A carpet's *face weight* is the number of ounces per square yard of carpet pile. (This figure does not include the weight of the backing or adhesive.) When taken into account with a carpet's density, the face weight gives the designer a good indication of how well a carpet will perform.

PILE HEIGHT

Pile height refers to the actual height, in inches, of the pile or tufts above the backing. Although the general rule of thumb is the deeper the pile, the more luxurious it feels underfoot, keep in mind that deeper pile also has a greater tendency to lay down or crush.

A SET OF SAMPLE SPECIFICATIONS FOR A TYPICAL COMMERCIAL-GRADE CARPET. THESE USUALLY APPEAR ON THE BACK OR UNDERSIDE OF THE DISPLAY FOLDERS THAT CONTAIN THE CARPETING SAMPLES.

STARTECH

SPECIFICATION

CONSTRUCTION:	TUFTED
SURFACE TEXTURE:	CUT PILE
GAUGE:	1/10 INCH
STITCH COUNT:	9.4 PER INCH
PILE HEIGHT:	.250 INCH
FACE YARN:	NYLON
DYE SYSTEM:	YARN DYED
FACE WEIGHT:	36 OUNCES PER SQUARE YARD
YARN COUNT:	1245/3; 1245/2
PRIMARY BACK:	WOVEN POLYPROPYLENE
SECONDARY BACK:	WOVEN POLYPROPYLENE
TOTAL WEIGHT:	78.1 OUNCES PER SQUARE YARD
WIDTH:	12 FEET

COLORING AND DYEING PROCESSES

One of carpeting's most favorable characteristics is the large variety of colors it offers. The myriad of choices now available enables designers to coordinate carpeting with existing or new materials and finishes with greater success than ever before, making the dyeing process a crucial part of carpet manufacturing. There are several methods used to color the yarn used in a carpet's manufacture; each can affect its look, price, and performance. By making used of these processes, a variety of carpets can be made to fit most interior design situations.

SOLUTION DYEING

The first opportunity to apply color to a fiber is when it is being manufactured or extruded. This process can't be used on natural fibers such as cotton or wool because the manufacturer has little control over their color other than what occurs naturally. Because man-made fibers are created from mixtures of chemicals and natural substances, pigments can be introduced into the mixture before the fibers are formed. This process is called *solution dyeing.* When the molten fiber of nylon, for example, is colored with a pigmented solution before it is extruded, the color is consistent throughout the entire fiber. This gives the finished carpet excellent lightfast and color-retentive properties. Carpets made with solution-dyed yarns can withstand cleaning with strong chemicals and resist fading as a result of exposure to sunlight, and so would work well in areas of heavy foot traffic or intense sun exposure.

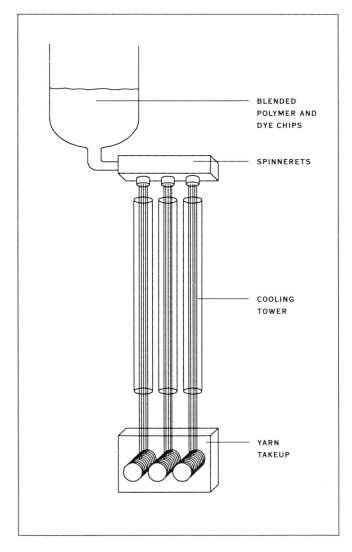

BLENDED POLYMER AND DYE CHIPS

SPINNERETS

COOLING TOWER

YARN TAKEUP

THE SOLUTION-DYEING PROCESS: AFTER THE FIBER MIXTURE IS HEATED AND BLENDED WITH SOLID DYE CHIPS IN A LARGE VAT, THE COLORED FIBER IS EXTRUDED THROUGH SPINNERETS AND DRIED IN A COOLING TOWER. THE YARN IS COLLECTED ON LARGE SPINDLES, THEN SET ASIDE UNTIL THE CARPET IS READY TO BE MANUFACTURED.

The main drawbacks to solution dyeing are the cost of the yarn and the time and effort involved in cleaning and changing the machinery between each color batch. Although the colors available for solution-dyed yarns in the past were somewhat limited, recent improvements in chemicals and mixing methods have increased their number somewhat. Another new development is the blending of two or three colors of fibers when the yarn is spun, which yields a soft, slightly heathered look that has become quite popular.

STOCK DYEING

In this coloring process, the raw fiber, either natural or man-made, is placed in a 5,000-pound stainless-steel vat to which a dye solution is added and boiled for 3 to 4 hours. Pumps circulate the dye during this period to ensure uniformity of color. When the correct shade has been achieved, the solution is drained and the fibers are washed, removed from the vat, and dried. The primary advantage to this method of dyeing is the consistency of the color throughout the individual fibers as well as the entire batch or dye lot. If a very large amount of fiber in one color is needed, numerous batches are mixed and blended when the fiber is spun into yarn because the color of each dye lot is slightly—though not imperceptibly—different. The colors are essentially the same, but when the fiber from one dye lot is placed next to another a difference is apparent. The blending process that takes place during spinning creates yarns that are essentially uniform. The disadvantage of stock dyeing is that manufacturers must stock large amounts of each colored fiber to ensure that ongoing orders will be fulfilled.

YARN OR SKEIN DYEING

The next opportunity to add color presents itself after the fibers have been spun into yarn. This process is referred to as *yarn* or *skein dyeing*. After the spinning process is complete, the yarn is wound into large loops called *skeins*. The process of yarn dyeing is similar to stock dyeing in most aspects except that the skeins are suspended into the vat on large hooks or arms. Once the correct color has been achieved, the yarn is washed and dried.

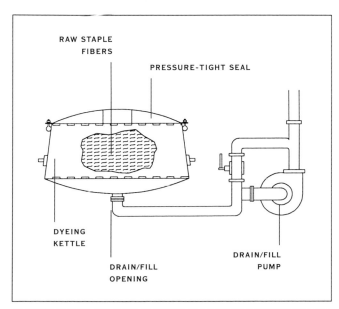

IN STOCK DYEING, THE FIBER IS BOILED IN A CONTINUOUSLY CIRCULATING DYE SOLUTION FOR 3 TO 4 HOURS, THEN WASHED AND DRIED. INDIVIDUAL BATCHES OF EACH COLOR ARE THEN SPUN TOGETHER TO ACHIEVE A CONSISTENT AND UNIFORM COLOR BLEND.

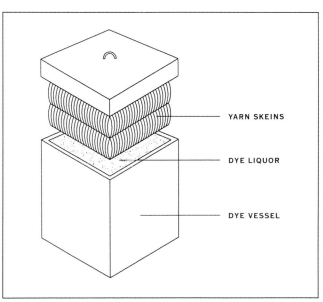

IN YARN OR SKEIN DYEING, SKEINS OF YARN ARE HELD IN VESSELS OF DYE UNTIL THE DESIRED COLOR HAS BEEN ATTAINED.

Yarn dyeing's main advantage is that the carpet manufacturer can buy less expensive uncolored yarn, dye it in their own facilities to their own specifications, and then use it to manufacture a carpet, thereby exchanging a stock of several batches of many different colors for one large amount of undyed yarn.

In *space dyeing,* another method of yarn dyeing, the yarn travels along rollers that move the yarn through a chemical steam bath and then through several sections of a huge press where various colors are printed onto the yarn in a random pattern. The yarn is then rinsed and dried.

PRINTED DESIGNS

Printing designs onto tufted carpet can, to some degree, imitate the woven or tufted patterns discussed above. The kitchen carpeting that was popular in the late 1970s and early 1980s used printed designs for many of their patterns. More recently, some manufacturers use what is called an *overprint process,* where an already finished colored carpet is printed with a geometric pattern. These companion designs are used as border carpets in hallways or to create interesting effects in large open areas.

IN SPACING DYEING, THE GRIEGE SUPPLY YARNS ARE FIRST RUN THROUGH A CHEMICAL STEAM BATH, THEN THROUGH A PRESS THAT PRINTS THE COLOR ONTO THE YARN.

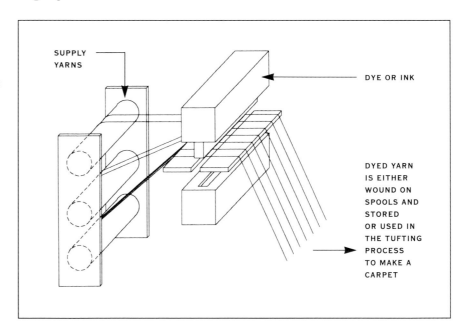

SUPPLY YARNS

DYE OR INK

DYED YARN IS EITHER WOUND ON SPOOLS AND STORED OR USED IN THE TUFTING PROCESS TO MAKE A CARPET

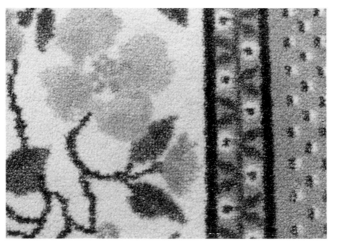

AN EXAMPLE OF A PRINTED CARPET, WHERE A COLORED CARPET IS OVERPRINTED WITH A DESIGN.

PIECE DYEING

The final opportunity that a manufacturer has to color carpet yarn is after it has been tufted onto its primary backing. The partially finished (without the secondary backing), undyed product is referred to as *greige goods*. There are two types of piece dyeing: *vat* or *beck dyeing* and *continuous dyeing*.

In vat dyeing, a large piece of carpet is joined into a continuous loop that is threaded around a reel inside a large stainless-steel vat. The carpet is then circulated through a continuously boiling dye solution for three to four hours. When finished, the carpet is washed and then removed to be dried. The primary advantage of this method is that the manufacturer can store large amounts of the undyed product without having to worry about having the appropriate stock of colors to fill orders in a timely manner. Vat dyeing's main disadvantage is that each dye lot yields a maximum of only about 1,000 yards, which can lead to problems when large quantities of carpet are required for projects with many open areas.

This problem is solved with the continuous dyeing method. In this process, the undyed carpet is prewashed through a system of rollers. An applicator evenly applies a specific amount of dye across the carpet as it is fed through the machine. The carpet then enters a steam-fixation chamber, where the dye is fixed into the carpet yarns. Finally, the carpet is washed and dried. This dyeing method eliminates small dye lots because the machinery can only accept a length of continuous carpet. Additional advantages are that the carpet can be dyed much faster, which results in reduced energy costs for the manufacturer.

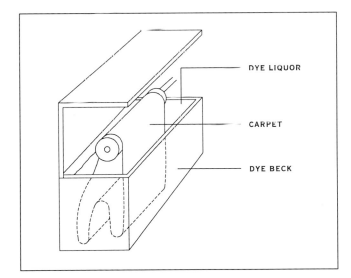

DYE LIQUOR

CARPET

DYE BECK

THE TWO METHODS OF PIECE DYEING BOTH UTILIZE GRIEGE GOODS. IN VAT OR BECK DYEING *(LEFT)*, A LARGE LOOP OF CARPET IS CIRCULATED THROUGH HEATED DYE. IN CONTINUOUS DYEING *(BELOW)*, THE UNDYED CARPET IS FED VIA A SYSTEM OF ROLLERS, WHERE THE DYE IS APPLIED AND MADE PERMANENT BY A STEAM TREATMENT.

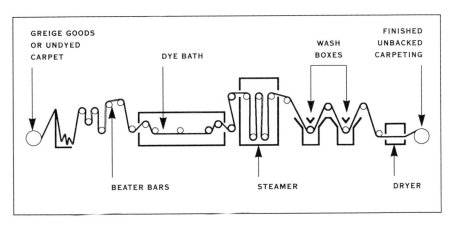

GREIGE GOODS OR UNDYED CARPET

DYE BATH

WASH BOXES

FINISHED UNBACKED CARPETING

BEATER BARS

STEAMER

DRYER

CARPET PADDING

The term *carpet padding* refers to any soft or cushiony material that is installed between the carpeting and the floor surface. The padding is specified primarily to enhance the performance characteristics of the carpet. There are several kinds of padding available, most of which fall into one of the following categories: felt or hair, sponge rubber, or urethane foam. In addition, there are a few other types of padding, which are discussed separately.

FELT OR HAIR PADS

This type of pad is composed of either animal hair or non-animal fibers, or a combination of the two. A rubberized or plastic coating may be applied to one or both sides to facilitate installation. They are manufactured by the needle punch process to create a feltlike cushion that has a dense feel underfoot. Classified by weight, felt or hair padding is graded from 32 to 86 ounces per square yard and can be purchased in widths of up to 12 feet.

SPONGE RUBBER PADS

Sponge rubber padding is manufactured with either a flat, smooth surface or a wafflelike or variegated surface. Both have a synthetic facing material on one side that improves handling during installation. This type of padding, which can feel soft or dense underfoot, can accommodate a range of traffic conditions, depending on the grade. *Flat rubber padding* is graded by its thickness, from $1/8$ to $5/16$ inch, in $1/16$-inch increments. *Waffle padding* is graded by weight, from 40 to 120 ounces per square yard. Both are available in widths up to 12 feet.

URETHANE FOAM PADS

There are three categories of urethane foam padding: prime foam, densified foam, and bonded prime foam. *Prime foam* is composed of polymeric materials. The foam is then cut into continuous sheets, and a facing material is laminated to one side. Its densities range from slightly more than 1 to 6 pounds per cubic foot. *Densified urethane foam* is produced in a similar manner but has a slightly different cell structure. A liquid form of the foam is poured into large "buns" of a specified density, then cut into the desired thickness. The facing material again is added to ease installation. Densities for this product range from about 3 to 6 pounds per cubic foot. *Bonded prime urethane* or *rebond padding* consists of trimmings or scraps of prime foam which is shredded into small pieces and then bonded to a urethane binder. The resulting product is then cut and the backing is applied. Bonded prime urethane padding ranges in density from 4 to 10 pounds per cubic foot (thickness of $1/4$ to $3/4$ inch), which can serve a range of traffic situations.

OTHER TYPES OF PADS

There are several other padding types, including foam rubber, polyester pneumatic cellular fiber, and resinated synthetic fiber. These make up the rest of the market but are not as common as those discussed above.

HAIR PADDING OVERVIEW AND CROSS SECTION.

FELT PADDING OVERVIEW AND CROSS SECTION.

FLAT SPONGE RUBBER PADDING OVERVIEW AND CROSS SECTION.

WAFFLE SPONGE RUBBER PADDING OVERVIEW AND CROSS SECTION.

 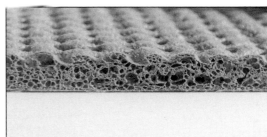

DENSIFIED URETHANE FOAM PADDING OVERVIEW AND CROSS SECTION.

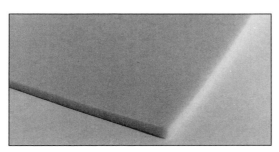 

BONDED PRIME URETHANE OR REBOND PADDING OVERVIEW AND CROSS SECTION.

MEASURING AND ESTIMATING

Estimating the necessary amount of carpet and the required installation charges for a project are fairly straightforward procedures. An interior designer should be familiar with these procedures so that every installation can be completed with as few problems as possible. Reviewing quantities and prices before installation and ordering will be time well spent.

Obviously, the first thing that a designer must determine is the required quantity of carpeting (and padding, if necessary) for the job by calculating the square footage of the area to be carpeted. Since carpeting is usually ordered by the square yard, this figure must be divided by 9 to yield the square yardage. This will give the designer a rough idea of the amount of carpeting that will be required. Many designers tack on an additional 10 to 15 percent to account for the waste that inevitably occurs; experience will help the designer more accurately determine the percentage of estimated waste. If the area is enclosed in one large room without hallways, odd corners, or stairs, this resulting figure should be close to what is required. Most spaces, however, have unique variations that require closer inspection.

Since most carpeting is manufactured in 12-foot widths, and the majority of installations are not evenly divisible by 12, it must be assumed that some piecing and seaming will be necessary and that there will be some waste. The judgments as to the number and placement of the seams is left mostly to the installer, who usually consults with the designer. The best solution—which would mean a minimum of seams and waste—is to mark out the placement of the carpet in widths and pieces on a scaled floor plan. Unfortunately, this is not as easy as it sounds: Usually, the fewer seams and pieces, the more waste; more seams and pieces means less waste. This is further complicated by the fact that the adjacent pieces of carpeting must run in the same direction.

The estimate must also include labor charges. Most installers charge a fixed amount per square yard of carpeting installed onto flat surfaces. Charges for all "nonstandard" installations, such as stairs, coves, or carpet bases, are additional. The estimate should also take into account the installation costs for any other unusual carpeting treatments, such as covering part or all of a piece of casework or using more than one pattern or a special border in a single room or corridor. Finally, the designer should also keep in mind that, in many instances, charges for installation are also based on the type that is specified—tackless, direct glue-down, or some other method.

Unless a job is relatively small or confined to a single unbroken space, a designer's figures will only provide an estimate. However, in order to avoid estimating jobs significantly lower or higher than their final costs, designers should continually work to refine their estimating procedures, making sure that at the conclusion of each job the "soft" numbers calculated at its start are more accurate than the last. Before ordering the carpeting, the designer should ask the installer to measure the job to determine the required yardage, and include any tackless (see the section on installation below), adhesives, moldings, or other elements in his or her price for installation. If a designer is reasonably familiar with the installation process, he or she can work with the installer to minimize omissions and problems.

INSTALLATION

Carpet installation is the process by which the carpet is attached or laid on the floor in a manner appropriate to the recommendations of the manufacturer and the common industry practices for the rate of expected wear. There are two standard methods of installation: tackless installation with padding and direct glue-down installation without padding. There also are a few less common methods.

TACKLESS INSTALLATION

When a carpet is to be installed with padding, *tackless installation* is usually recommended. This process begins with the installation of *tackless* or *tack strips*, which are small wood strips about the size of a yard stick with numerous sharp barbs protruding through the surface. These strips are attached to the floor, with the barbs facing upward, around the perimeter of the space to be carpeted. The padding is positioned to the edge of the tackless, and either stapled or spot-glued to the floor to keep it from moving around when the carpet is pulled or stretched over it. The carpet is laid over the padding, attached to the tackless at one end of the space, and stretched tightly and evenly with a kicker or a power stretcher. The carpet is then hooked to the tackless on the opposite side of the room. This procedure is repeated several times to ensure an even, tight installation with no wrinkles or bubbles. The carpet is then trimmed at the edges and vacuumed.

DIRECT GLUE-DOWN INSTALLATION

Because the carpeting will be glued directly to the floor in this type of installation, the preparation of the gluing surface is extremely important. The floor must be clean and dry. If it has been painted or covered in any way, it must be tested to ensure that the adhesive will stick properly. The adhesive is then applied as recommended by the manufacturer; usually in sections small enough to facilitate installation and seaming without it drying too quickly. The designer should be absolutely certain that the correct adhesive is being used for the specified carpet and the floor surface to which it will be attached.

OTHER INSTALLATION METHODS

There a few other installation methods that are becoming increasingly popular. One of these is a combination of the tackless and direct glue-down methods, a result of the recent decline of carpeting with an integral high-density foam padding. In this method, a pad is glued to the floor with a special adhesive, then the carpet is glued directly to the surface of the pad. This method enables the designer to be more selective in choosing a pad to match the estimated wear the carpet will receive, and has the strength and stability of a direct glue-down installation.

Another alternate installation method is the *free-lay method*, which is used primarily with carpet tiles. A strip of releasable adhesive is applied to the floor every 10 or 20 feet in both directions. While the weight of the tiles tends to hold each unit of carpet flat and in place, the tiles that are laid directly on the adhesive resist lateral movement and help to keep all adjacent tiles in place.

9

PAINT
AND OTHER
INTERIOR
COATINGS

COMPOSITION

Most paints or coatings are composed of four elements—vehicle, body, pigment, and additives—each of which contributes to a coating's properties and overall performance. If an element is changed in any way, or if the ratio or formulation of elements is altered, the properties of the coating will be affected.

THE VEHICLE

The vehicle, which makes up the liquid portion of the coating, is a combination of a *binder* and a *solvent* or *thinner*. It gives the body of the coating consistency and continuity and increases its adhesive properties. (See "The Body," later in this chapter.)

BINDERS

The binder is the essentially transparent, nonvolatile portion of the vehicle that holds the pigment particles together to form the cured surface film. It is so crucial to the quality and durability of a coating that most are classified by binder type.

Oil binders. The oldest form of binder, which is still in use today. The standard oil binder is linseed oil, although other oils are also used. While oil-based coatings are still reasonably durable and cost-effective, they have been all but replaced by alkyd- and latex-based coatings, which are less messy, smelly, and moisture-intolerant.

Alkyd binders. The alkyd-based coatings contain oil-modified resins that dry by means of oxidation, and have most of the advantages of oil-based coatings with few of the problems. They are available in a wide range of colors and finishes and can be applied over most surfaces. They are probably the most popular of all coating types. The combination of linseed oil and alkyd resins used in *oil-alkyd binders* improves hardness, reduces drying time, and prevents fading. Oil-alkyd paints are used primarily as enamels for exterior trim.

Latex binders. Latex-based coatings are quickly becoming the most common in commercial interiors. These water-soluble products can be thinned and cleaned up with water, and dry by means of evaporation. As the water evaporates, the pigment and binder coalesce into a tough, insoluble film. In most environments they are as durable as alkyd-based coatings, have little odor, are not flammable, and have excellent color-retentive properties.

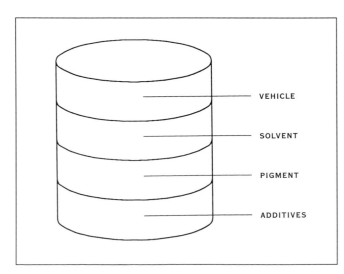

THE PROPORTION OF INGREDIENTS IN A TYPICAL OPAQUE PAINT.

VEHICLE

SOLVENT

PIGMENT

ADDITIVES

Other binders. Oleoresinous binders, a combination of hard resins and drying oils, are most commonly used in varnish. Because they tend to yellow with age, their popularity has recently been on the decline. *Phenolic binders* use a synthetic resin to create a coating similar to oleoresin. They are available in clear and pigmented versions, in both flat or high-gloss finishes. Note that when used on exteriors, however, they do tend to darken over time. *Rubber-based binders* are formed from resins derived from synthetic rubber. They dry rapidly and are highly resistant to water and some chemicals. They are an excellent choice for such high-moisture interior areas as kitchens and laundry and shower rooms as well as over exterior masonry. Urethane was once used exclusively as a varnish substitute on exterior surfaces and interior floor surfaces. A fairly recent development that is increasing in popularity, *urethane-based binders* are similar to alkyd binders but do an even better job. Urethane-based paints are available in both oil-modified and oil-free versions.

There are other binders based on vinyl, silicone, and combinations of these and those described above, each of which has a variety of properties that fit many different uses. Many of these specialized coatings are designed for use in institutions where high wear, abrasion, or exposure to chemicals are considerations. Generally speaking, an evaluation of product specification sheets will indicate which coating types are suitable for a given situation. For special situations, the designer should follow the recommendations of a local supplier or manufacturer's representative, and have a basic understanding of the standard properties of mainstream coatings.

SOLVENTS

The solvent is the part of the coating that holds the binder and pigments in suspension while they cure or dry and form a film. The solvent also controls the rate of evaporation or oxidation, thereby regulating the appropriate drying time needed for each type of coating. Finally, the solvent thins the coating to a uniform consistency that ensures easy application. If a coating is too thin, it may be difficult to apply, or it may not cover the surface satisfactorily so that several coats may be necessary. If a coating is too thick, it may not stir thoroughly, dry correctly, or spread evenly, and the uniform distribution of color pigments would also be hindered. The nature and quality of the solvent has a direct bearing on the amount of paint that is necessary, and thus affects the cost of a job.

There are two primary types of solvents—*hydrocarbon* or oil-based and *oxygenated* or water-based—which correspond to the two major categories of binders. A third type, based on terpene solvents, which are derived from turpentine or pine oil, is used only on a limited basis.

THE AMOUNT AND TYPE OF SOLVENT CONTROLS THE COATING'S CONSISTENCY, WHICH DIRECTLY AFFECTS ITS QUALITY DURING APPLICATION. IF A SINGLE APPLICATION IS TOO THICK, IT WILL DRY SLOWLY AND UNEVENLY, AND RESULT IN UNEVEN COLOR AFTER CURING. IF THE APPLICATION IS TOO THIN, THE SUBSTRATE WILL SHOW THROUGH, POSSIBLY REQUIRING MORE COATS THAN WERE ORIGINALLY BUDGETED FOR.

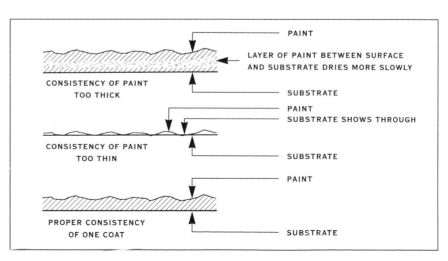

THE PIGMENT

Because it is clearly evident in a coating's color, the pigment is the most immediately recognizable part of its composition. A coating's pigment is composed of solid particles of equal size that are suspended in the vehicle.

The rules that govern pigments and color generally also apply to paints and coatings. Because all objects and surfaces absorb and reflect the electromagnetic waves of the spectrum of white light, the color of a particular coating is also a manifestation of the phenomena of absorption and reflection. For example, red paint absorbs all wavelengths of light except for red, which it reflects, thus producing the color red. Since every color absorbs and reflects different areas of the spectrum, we can assume that when two or more colors are mixed together, the result will be a third color that accurately represents the sum of the proportion of each color. However, the other elements of a coating also affect the color of the dry pigment when they are combined. As a result, coating manufacturers invest considerable time and money in determining the exact formulation for each color in their product line.

Pigments are classified by the materials from which they are derived: either *organic* or *inorganic*. In most cases, more than one type of pigment is used to create a specific color. For example, there are at least eight different materials that can be used to create the color red. Each pigment has characteristics that directly affect blending, mixing, lightfastness, and other coating properties.

Pigments also contribute to a coating's opacity (also referred to as *hide* or *hiding power*), which is the extent to which a coating can cover the substrate without show-through. One way that a coating's opacity is enhanced is by *shading* the paint. This is done by adding a dark pigment such as lamp black to the mixture, so that the final color has depth as well as increased opacity, and lessens the need for expensive body materials (see "The Body," page 158).

TYPICAL COATING PIGMENTS		
COLOR	**ORGANIC**	**INORGANIC**
RED	TOLUIDINE MONASTRAL	IRON OXIDE MOLYBDENUM CADMIUM
ORANGE		RED IRON OXIDE MOLYBDENUM ORANGE
YELLOW	HANSA	YELLOW IRON OXIDE CHROME YELLOW ZINC CHROMATE NICKEL TITANATE
BLUE	ULTRAMARINE BLUE PHTHALOCYANINE BLUE	PRUSSIAN BLUE
BLACK	LAMP BLACK CARBON BLACK	
METALLIC		ALUMINUM FLAKE ZINC DUST STAINLESS STEEL DUST

Gloss, another important coating characteristic, also depends on the size of the particles of pigment and the ratio of pigment to binder. Most coatings are grouped into somewhat flexible categories based on the degree of gloss exhibited, such as high gloss, semigloss, eggshell or low luster, and flat. These terms refer to the amount of light that is reflected from the dried coating's surface. For example, a high-gloss coating, which has relatively small pigment particles, yields a smoother finish texture that reflects a great deal of light; on the other hand, a flat-finish coating, which has larger pigment particles, reflects very little.

The colorless binder acts as a glue, holding the pigment particles together until the mixture has cured. When the proportion of binder in a coating is increased, the amount of pigment is decreased and the result is a smoother, glossier surface. Conversely, when there is less binder and more pigment, then more of the pigment sticks up through the binder and the pigment particles lie closer together, creating a rougher surface with less gloss. Because high-gloss coatings are usually more durable and easier to clean, they are commonly used on surfaces that will encounter the most abuse, such as base trims or moldings around doors and windows. Flat-finish coatings are desirable where color is of primary importance and where reflections should be kept to a minimum, such as ceilings and many walls. While they are not as durable as high-gloss coatings, they do help to hide surface imperfections and blemishes. The semigloss and eggshell finishes each have characteristics that satisfy the various requirements of the remainder of the market. *Flat enamel*, a relatively new finish, combines the antiglare characteristics of flat coatings with the durability of high-gloss coatings. Its formulation is similar to high-gloss products but includes additives such as silica that dull the gloss and create a flatter finish.

A PAINTED SURFACE ABSORBS ALL THE COLORS WITHIN THE SPECTRUM OF WHITE LIGHT, AND REFLECTS THE COLOR OR COLORS OF ITS PIGMENT. IN ADDITION, THE CURED SURFACE'S DEGREE OF GLOSS AFFECTS THE EXTENT TO WHICH IT REFLECTS LIGHT: A GLOSS COATING, WHICH HAS RELATIVELY SMALL, EVENLY DISTRIBUTED PIGMENT PARTICLES, REFLECTS A GREAT DEAL OF LIGHT, WHILE A FLAT COATING, WHICH HAS LARGER, MORE IRREGULARLY SHAPED PIGMENT PARTICLES, REFLECTS VERY LITTLE.

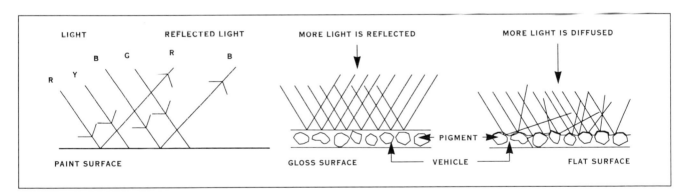

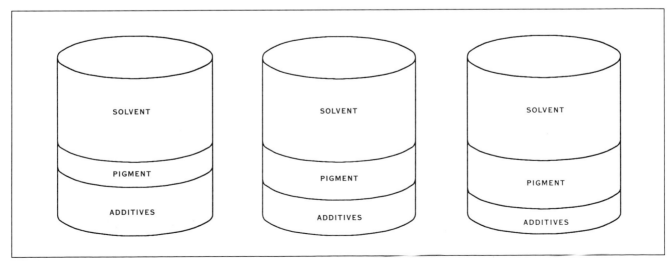

THE PROPORTION OF INGREDIENTS IN A TYPICAL GLOSS ENAMEL PAINT *(LEFT)*, SEMIGLOSS PAINT *(CENTER)*, AND FLAT PAINT *(RIGHT)*.

THE BODY

The body, which is usually composed of white metallic salts, provides the majority of the coating film. Lead carbonate was once used in all paints, but exposure to lead has been shown to cause brain damage and dysfunction so its use is now prohibited. Zinc oxide, which is safe, is used in many lower-quality coatings; higher-quality paints usually contain titanium dioxide, which has excellent hiding properties. Some manufacturers add extenders such as calcium carbonate or talc, which enables them to use fewer of the more expensive ingredients and still achieve the required opacity. The presence of extenders in a coating formulation does not indicate inferiority. In reasonable amounts, extenders provide an effective means of achieving reasonable hiding characteristics without adding unnecessary cost, and are also used to decrease gloss. However, there is a limit to the amount of extenders that can be added to the mixture. If the proportion of extenders is too high, the wearability and the quality of the finish will be negatively influenced.

ADDITIVES

Additives are those coating components that modify the characteristics of the pigment and/or the binder, and are used to adapt standard coating formulations to suit a variety of situations.

One of the most common additives, *driers* significantly reduce a coating's evaporation or oxidation time to a more reasonable period. For instance, without driers most alkyd paints would take up to a week to cure completely. With a drier added, an alkyd paint will cure within 12 to 18 hours. *Anti-skinning agents* are added to create quick-drying paints. They are used to prevent the formation of a skin on the surface of the paint while it is still in the can, and disappear or evaporate during application. *Coalescing agents* aid latex paints in the drying process. As the coating cures, the latex particles tend to group together as the coating forms a film. This additive encourages the particles to group together uniformly, resulting in a smooth, even surface.

Pigmentation agents, suspension agents, and *wetting agents* all affect the character of the pigment. Suspension agents prevent the pigment from settling to the bottom of the can, where they would bind together and become unusable. Wetting agents enhance the binder's ability to completely coat each pigment particle, ensuring even color distribution and film formation.

Viscosity-control agents regulate a coating's thickness to the proper consistency. *Thixotropic agents* give a coating a variable body that will conform to a variety of application techniques. *Preservatives* retard or eliminate the growth of bacteria that would either damage the coating or cause health problems.

OTHER TYPES OF COATINGS

While paint—which usually dries to an opaque finish—is generally considered to be the principal coating type, there are several transparent and semitransparent coating products about which an interior designer should be aware.

Varnishes are transparent coatings composed of resins (for hardness and reduced drying time), drying oils (for durability and flexibility), a solvent, and a dryer. This category of coating includes the traditional natural-resin varnishes as well as the newer "urethane," or modified alkyd resin, coatings. If durability is a primary consideration, urethane coatings offer superior hard surface characteristics that resist yellowing and have the added flexibility of the natural resins. The addition of epoxy resins can increase durability even further. Varnishes are available in gloss and matte (usually referred to as satin) finishes.

Transparent varnishes are described in terms of their oil "length," which refers to the mixture's ratio of oil to resin. *Short oil varnishes*, which have more resin and less oil, are quick drying and have a hard finish. *Long oil varnishes*, which have more oil and less resin, have a longer drying time and a softer, more elastic finish. Both of these varnish varieties are generally used on exterior surfaces. *Medium oil varnishes*, which fall somewhere in between, are considered to be multipurpose, interior-use products.

Stains, which fall somewhere between opaque paints and transparent varnishes, contain pigments that dry to a semitransparent finish. When the stain is applied to the substrate (which is normally wood), the low-viscosity oil soaks into the surface. After drying, the residue is wiped off, leaving oil and pigment in the pores. In this manner, wood can be stained or colored while leaving the wood's natural grain exposed. This surface can then be left as is, oiled, or coated with a clear finish. Because the oil and pigment that penetrate into the surface increase its resistance to the effects of the elements, stains are popular as an exterior finish. Petroleum-based stains provide further defense against molds and insects; however, as a result of their questionable environmental effects, their use is no longer widespread.

Lacquers contain an extremely volatile solvent, and thus dry as soon as the solvent has evaporated, permitting frequent application for a deep, rich finish. As a result, they are usually applied under very controlled conditions to ensure consistent quality. Their high-gloss finish, which can be either transparent or pigmented, is extremely hard. Lacquer is particularly popular among furniture manufacturers.

A MANUFACTURER'S SELECTION OF PENETRATING STAINS, SHOWING THE WIDE VARIETY OF COLORS AND GLOSSES AVAILABLE.

THE PROPORTION OF INGREDIENTS IN A TYPICAL TRANSPARENT VARNISH *(NEAR RIGHT)* AND PENETRATING STAIN *(FAR RIGHT)*.

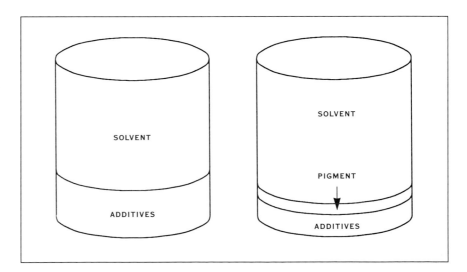

Primers compose a subcategory of coating that fills an important behind-the-scenes role. A primer's main function is to increase adhesion between the substrate and the coating. It is designed to be applied directly to the bare substrate. While certain special primers, such as those that inhibit rust, are used to protect the substrate, they are not a substitute for preliminary surface preparation, although they can minimize the need for it somewhat. It should be noted that the primer really only enhances the coating's ability to adhere to the surface, and that adequate preparation of the substrate is always an important installation factor.

There are two common types of specialized primers: sealers and fillers. A *sealer* is designed to adequately seal a porous substrate such as wood in one application. There are two reasons for this. First, a porous surface will immediately absorb almost any coating before it can dry, including a standard primer, thus defeating the purpose of the product. As a result, two or more coats of a standard primer may be necessary in order to adequately seal the surface. On the other hand, a sealer will stabilize before it can be sucked into the surface, thereby successfully sealing the material in one coat. Second, some wood surfaces contain natural dyes or chemicals that migrate into the coating during the drying process, causing discoloration. A sealer creates an impermeable barrier between the substrate and the coating, helping to preserve the intended finish or color.

A *filler* is used to smooth or fill out the texture of the substrate. If its pores or texture will hinder final finish of the selected coating—which is sometimes the case with concrete, masonry, and some types of wood—the surface of the substrate can be made reasonably smooth. A filler would also be used when a wood surface will be finished with a high gloss, such as might be required for paneling in a conference room or formal reception area. A primer sealer would be used first, however, to seal the surface and leave a texture that will enable the coating that follows to adhere properly.

THESE CROSS-SECTION DRAWINGS SHOW THE DIFFERENCE BETWEEN FILLERS AND SEALERS: FILLERS ARE USED TO SMOOTH OR FILL OUT THE TEXTURE OF THE SUBSTRATE, AND SEALERS ARE DESIGNED TO ADEQUATELY SEAL—BUT NOT ALTER THE TEXTURE OR CHARACTER OF—A POROUS SUBSTRATE SUCH AS WOOD IN ONE APPLICATION.

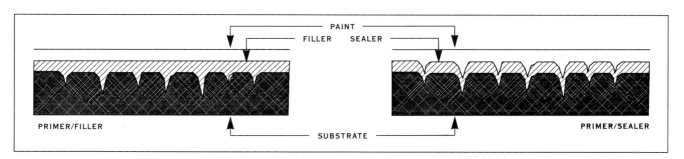

PRIMER/FILLER

PRIMER/SEALER

THE PROPORTION OF INGREDIENTS IN A TYPICAL SEALER (*NEAR RIGHT*) AND FILLER (*FAR RIGHT*).

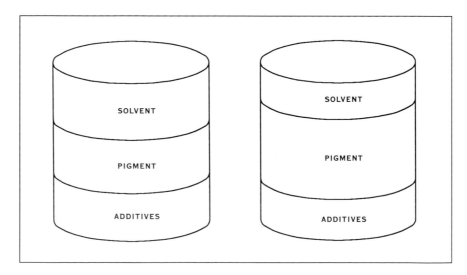

THE PAINTING PROCESS

The successful performance of a paint or coating is integrally related to the preparation of the substrate surface and the application of the recommended primer, sealer, and number of coats of the specific coating.

SURFACE PREPARATION

The proper preparation of any coating surface should be an interior designer's first concern. He or she should be familiar with basic surface preparation procedures so that each step is considered during the specification process. In most cases, a good painting contractor can prevent a host of potential problems by preparing the substrate as recommended by the coating manufacturer. In general, the substrate should be clean, dry, and free from any foreign material such as dust, dirt, or wax, so that anything that might hinder the adhesion of a coating has been removed before painting begins.

It is imperative that an interior designer review the manufacturer's recommendations or instructions before making a final coating selection to ensure that all special requirements have been taken into account. In most instances, nothing more than a light sanding is necessary. However, if a surface will be subjected to harsh or unusual conditions, or if a coating will be applied to an atypical surface, the designer should be sure that the most obvious problems or conflicts are resolved and properly specified. Because they use the products on a daily basis, a local paint supplier or painting contractor can provide a wealth of information. If, however, a manufacturer's representative or a contractor recommends a procedure that is contrary to the published data, get another opinion. Specifying a given substrate's recommended coatings or paints, primers, surface preparation, and method of application should minimize problems and maximize quality.

COVERAGE AND ESTIMATING

Regardless of its content, every coating is designed to cover a surface at a specified rate. This information, which is usually published by the manufacturer, indicates a range of square feet of surface area, from a minimum to a maximum amount per gallon, that the coating can be expected to cover. Since each type of coating has a different viscosity and composition, each spreads onto a surface at a different rate and thickness. Most coatings require at least two coats to cover a new, unfinished surface. Interior designers should be somewhat familiar with these figures for the purposes of estimating and budgeting, though the actual amount of paint is usually not included in either the specifications or the budget. That is determined by the painting contractor, whose *area take-off*, or calculation of the square footage of a space based on an evaluation of the floor plan, is used to calculate the exact amount required.

When estimating the amount of paint required for a particular job, the area of the surface to be covered is calculated to a number of square feet, which is then divided by the recommended coverage rate in gallons per square feet. The result is the amount required for one coat of that product; multiplied by the number of coats, the result is the number of gallons required for that particular area. This figuring should also be done for the primer and sealer, if they are required.

Without a comprehensive set of standards, the specification of paint and coating products can be somewhat confusing. As has been emphasized at several points in this chapter, interior designers should use their common sense and experience, as well as the advice of contractors and manufacturers, to determine which coatings best suit a particular space.

10

WALLCOVERINGS

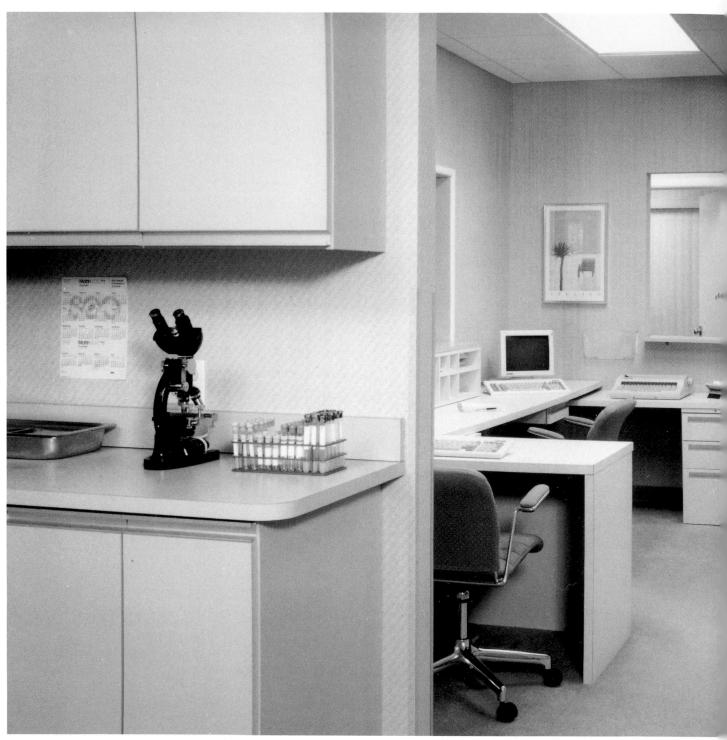

WALLCOVERINGS CAN BE USED TO SUBTLY ENHANCE A RANGE OF CONTRACT INTERIORS, PARTICULARLY WHEN THE ACCOMPANYING FINISH ELEMENTS HAVE BEEN CAREFULLY COORDINATED. *PHOTO COURTESY OF AVATAR DESIGN, INC.*

Next to paint, wallcoverings are the most popular method of finishing a wall surface, both residentially and commercially. Reasonably inexpensive, they are available in a wide variety of colors and textures, can increase the durability of a wall surface, and can set the mood for a space, from a single room to an entire project. With the many manufacturers that market wallcoverings to the interior design trades, this interior finish offers the contract interior designer a nearly unlimited field of design possibilities.

Wall surface materials constructed of paper were first used in Asia. Paper wallcoverings were printed to imitate other finishes, such as wood, brick, or marble, for far less than the cost of the actual materials. As printing techniques developed, as many as ten to twelve colors could be used to print complex and realistic motifs. The primary disadvantage of paper wallcoverings, then as now, is their lack of durability, particularly in areas of high wear. To increase the wearability of the paper, manufacturers began applying clear vinyl coatings to their products in the 1950s. While there are still many paper-based wallcoverings on the market, most commercial-grade wallcoverings are now made from vinyl. The available colors and patterns seem infinite, and the cost is comparatively affordable. If vinyl wallcovering is installed in the recommended manner and properly maintained, it will not only provide long-term durability but will retain its original look longer than any other competitively priced wallcovering or surface material.

VINYL WALLCOVERING COMPONENTS

All vinyl wallcoverings have either two or three components: (1) a backing, (2) a vinyl layer, and (3) an applied finish or coating of some type. When combined, these elements create a strong, durable wallcovering.

A wallcovering derives most of its strength from its backing. When a wallcovering is designed, the choice of backing is usually determined by the product's intended characteristics, such as strength, abrasive resistance, depth of pattern, embossing, and so on. The table on the opposite page lists the backing materials that are most often used in commercial wallcoverings.

The vinyl layer is composed of the following elements:

1. Polyvinylchloride (PVC) resins, for strength and abrasive resistance.

2. Plasticizers, for pliability and processability. Plasticizers can also improve a wallcovering's fire retardance, stain resistance, abrasive resistance, and aging characteristics. However, not every plasticizer provides these improvements to the same degree. Each manufacturer varies the configuration of the materials to create a wallcovering's desired characteristics.

3. Stabilizers, to help the vinyl resins maintain the correct colors when subjected to the light and heat of manufacturing during processing.

4. Pigments, to add color. Because all pigments do not react to the manufacturing process in the same way, the choice of pigments for a wallcovering is critical. Good-quality pigments can be a wallcovering's most costly element, which is usually why wallcoverings in darker, more intense colors, such as red, gold, and blue, are more costly than those produced in lighter colors.

5. Fillers, such as calcium carbonate, are sometimes used to create a particular look or to lower the cost.

6. Other additives, such as fungicides or fire retardants, usually in low levels.

The optional third layer is a polyvinylfluoride (PVF) film that creates a tough outer surface to protect the wallcovering. This coating is known by various trade names, including Tedlar. Wallcoverings with this coating are most desirable for areas where pens, markers, paints, and harsh cleaning materials are used regularly and may come in contact with the wall surface.

Vinyl wallcoverings are manufactured by two processes: calendaring or plastisol. Calendered vinyl wallcoverings are created by running the PVC over hot metal rollers that squeeze or flatten the hot compound into a film or sheet. This sheet can then either be stored and laminated to the fabric backing with an adhesive at a later date or attached directly onto the backing in one continuous step. The plastisol method involves spreading liquid PVC over the moving fabric backing by running the fabric under a knife and then fusing the two materials together at an extremely high temperature.

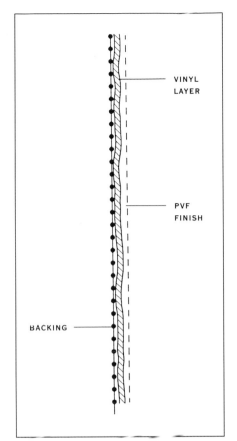

A CROSS-SECTION DRAWING SHOWING THREE COMPONENTS (TWO BASIC AND ONE OPTIONAL) OF A VINYL WALLCOVERING: THE BACKING, THE VINYL LAYER, AND THE PVF FINISH.

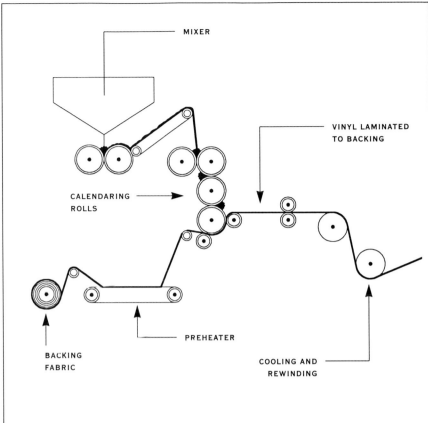

THE CALENDARING METHOD OF VINYL WALLCOVERING MANUFACTURING: THE PVC IS CALENDARED THROUGH A SERIES OF ROLLERS ONTO A PREHEATED BACKING, THEN LAMINATED, COOLED, AND WOUND ON LARGE SPOOLS.

NAME	CLASSIFICATION			WEIGHT OF BACKING (IN OUNCES)			
	LIGHT	MEDIUM	HEAVY	1	2	3	4
SCRIM	■			■			
NONWOVEN SCRIM	■			■■			
OSNABURG		■				■■	
NONWOVEN OSNABURG		■				■	
DRILL			■				■

TYPICAL WALLCOVERING BACKINGS

VINYL WALLCOVERING TYPES

Three categories are used as a comparative standard to specify vinyl wallcoverings: types I, II, and III, which are light, medium, and heavy duty, respectively. These three classifications meet a variety of decorating needs. However, they apply only to vinyl wallcoverings; when papers and fabrics are specified, wear is usually not a consideration.

Type I wallcoverings are usually manufactured on a scrim or nonwoven backing and weigh a total of 7 to 13 ounces per square yard. Type I wallcoverings can be installed in any area that does not receive a great amount of wear, such as an office or hospital room, and provide an economical aesthetic alternative to paint.

Type II wallcoverings are usually manufactured on an Osnaburg, Drill, or nonwoven backing, and weigh between 13 and 22 ounces per square yard. Type II wallcoverings are more durable than type I, and can be used in any public location, such as dining rooms, corridors, and classrooms, but are not recommended for areas of very high traffic.

Type III wallcoverings are manufactured on Drill fabric backing and weigh more than 22 ounces per square yard. These wallcoverings are designed for unusually high-traffic areas, such as hospital corridors, cafeterias, or elevator lobbies.

SPECIFYING VINYL WALLCOVERINGS

In some cases, it would be correct to assume that all that is required to specify a vinyl wallcovering is the manufacturer's name, the pattern name and number, and the color and its number. There are instances, however, where the interior designer must investigate other points: What materials were used to make the wallcovering? How thick is it? How well does it wear? In a hospital corridor, for example, a thin delicate vinyl would probably not be suitable, and a heavy-duty, one-color wallcovering would most likely be inappropriate in a corporate office.

For every pattern that is produced, its manufacturer publishes product data for comparative purposes. In cooperation with the U.S. government, the wallcovering industry has devised a set of product standards. When the designer is aware of how each specification characteristic affects a wallcovering, accurate specification is much easier.

WALLCOVERING TYPES AND CLASSIFICATIONS							
	CLASSIFICATION			PRODUCT WEIGHT RANGE (IN OUNCES)			
	LIGHT	MEDIUM	HEAVY	0	10	20	30
TYPE I	▬			▬▬▬			
TYPE II		▬			▬▬		
TYPE III			▬			▬▬➤	

As is mentioned above, wallcoverings are grouped into three categories based on minimum total weight requirements. The other criteria are as follows:

1. The *minimum coating weight* indicates the amount of vinyl that has been applied to the backing.

2. The *breaking strength*, which indicates a product's general durability, is a measurement of the force required to pull a section apart when pulling evenly.

3. The *tearing strength*, which indicates a product's resistance to tearing, measures the force required to tear a section when subjected to pressure at one particular point. An example of this would be when the edge of a desk that is being moved down a corridor hits the wall.

4. *Adhesion* measures the extent to which the wallcovering adheres to the substrate.

5. *Abrasion resistance* indicates the product's ability to resist wearing through to the backing when it is continually rubbed in one place. This would occur, for example, when the backs of folding chairs are pushed against a wall.

6. *Flame spread* and *smoke development* are two crucial points of a wallcovering's specifications. The number associated with the flame spread rating relates to how quickly a length of wallcovering will be engulfed by flames. The plasticizers, resins, pigments, and stabilizers that form the major part of a vinyl wallcovering all contribute to the way it reacts when subjected to fire. The rate of smoke development reflects the amount and speed with which smoke develops once the wallcovering begins to burn. Fire safety considerations became an important issue as vinyl wallcoverings gained popularity and came to be used in a wide range of settings, including such public environments such as large offices and hotels. As sometimes occurs with new products, unforseen problems arose: Some of the wallcoverings burned so rapidly that it was impossible to escape the flames once the fire started, or emitted toxic fumes such as cyanide gas. For both characteristics, there is a required maximum; the lower the number, the better the wallcovering will perform in these areas.

7. *Lightfastness* is a measure of the extent to which the product resists fading when subjected to light for an extended period of time. The requirement for all vinyl wallcoverings is that no change should occur.

8. Because wallcoverings are cut to fit snugly against adjacent ceilings and floors, and lengths of wallcovering are hung to meet in seams, *shrinkage*—the extent to which a product shrinks once it is exposed to water and subsequently dried—is an important concern. If a wallcovering shrinks more than an extremely limited amount, the wall behind will be exposed, resulting in an unprofessional, sloppy look. The standards shown in the table on the following page indicate the maximum percentage of shrinkage that is acceptable within the wallcovering specification.

9. The *cold crack* and *heat aging* tests ensure that a wallcovering will not become brittle or crack, discolor, or wrinkle when subjected to extremes of heat or cold within a given period of time. The requirements for both characteristics state that no changes should occur.

There are other vinyl wallcovering characteristics not covered in the standard specifications that, depending on the project, might also be of concern. For example, many manufacturers offer stain-resistant coatings (which are either standard or optional, depending on the product) that inhibit the absorption of such materials as shoe polish and lipstick and make the product easier to clean.

A few manufacturers offer wallcoverings that resist discoloring when cleaned with harsh chemicals or solutions such as alkaline soaps and bleach. This feature would be an important consideration in such high-traffic projects as schools, hospitals, and municipal offices.

A SET OF SAMPLE SPECIFICATIONS FOR A TYPICAL COMMERCIAL-GRADE WALLCOVERING.

SPACETECH

PHYSICAL PROPERTIES	U.S. UNITS	METRIC UNITS
TOTAL WEIGHT	21 OZ. PLY	651 G. PLM
	14 OZ. PSY	475 G. PSM
FABRIC WEIGHT	3 OZ. PLY	93 G. PLM
VINYL WEIGHT	18 OZ. PLY	558 G. PLM
ROLL WIDTH	53/54"	134/137 CM
VINYL GAUGE	9 MILS	0.23 MM
FABRIC	OSNABURG	
FEDERAL SPECIFICATION	CCC-W-408A, TYPE II	
CFFA SPECIFICATION	CFFA-W0101A, TYPE II, CLAS A	
U.L. RATING	(ASTM E-84 TUNNEL TEST)	
FLAME SPREAD	15	
SMOKE DEVELOPMENT	20	

STANDARD PHYSICAL PROPERTIES OF WALLCOVERING TYPES

REQUIREMENTS	TYPE I	TYPE II	TYPE III
TOTAL WEIGHT (MINIMUM OUNCES PER SQUARE YARD)	7	13	22
MINIMUM COATING WEIGHT (OUNCES PER SQUARE YARD)	5	7	12
BREAKING STRENGTH (MINIMUM POUNDS PER SQUARE YARD)			
WARP	40	50	100
FILLING	30	55	95
TEAR STRENGTH (MINIMUM SCALE READING)			
WARP	14	25	50
FILLING	12	25	50
ADHESION[1] (MINIMUM POUNDS PER INCH)	2	3	3
ABRASION RESISTANCE (DOUBLE RUBS)	200+	300+	1000+
FLAME SPREAD (MAXIMUM)	25	25	25
SMOKE DEVELOPMENT (MAXIMUM)	50	50	50
COLORFASTNESS TO LIGHT	NO CHANGE	NO CHANGE	NO CHANGE
BLOCKING (SCALE RATING MAXIMUM)	NO. 2	NO. 2	NO. 2
SHRINKAGE (PERCENT MAXIMUM)			
WARP	2.0	2.0	2.0
FILLING	1.0	1.0	1.5
COLD CRACK (@ 20°F)	NO CHANGE	NO CHANGE	NO CHANGE
HEAT AGING (7 DAYS @ 158°F)	[2]	[2]	[2]
CROCKING	GOOD	GOOD	GOOD

[1] NONWOVEN SUPPORTING MATERIALS SHALL BE BONDED TO THE WEARING SURFACE. WHEN AN ATTEMPT IS MADE TO PULL THE WEARING SURFACE FROM THE BACKING BY HAND, THE BACKING SHALL DELAMINATE OR BREAK BEFORE THE FAILURE OF THE BONDING.
[2] THE SPECIMEN SHALL NOT BECOME STIFF, BRITTLE, SOFT, TACKY, DISCOLORED, OR SHOW LOSS OF GRAIN.

CUSTOM WALLCOVERINGS

As the term implies, a custom wallcovering is designed to fit the interior designer's (and client's) specifications, and is manufactured to incorporate special colors, patterns, or physical dimensions into the finished product. When compared with the manufacturer's standard products, the time and effort required to create a custom wallcovering can increase its cost.

The two most common considerations in creating a custom wallcoverings are color and pattern. For example, a client may want to match a color in his or her corporate identity program, or a pattern's *colorways*, or sets of colors, may not match other finishes or furnishings. The designer may feel that a custom pattern would be more appropriate than those that the manufacturer has to offer, or the client will request that the company logo be included in the pattern.

There are a few points to keep in mind when specifying a custom wallcovering. Most manufacturers require a minimum order (usually 300 to 500 yards) before undertaking a custom product. The manufacturer may choose to absorb the usual additional charges for such items as set up, special designs or artwork, and special color formulation if the order is for 500 to 800 yards, though this varies from manufacturer to manufacturer. Many commercial projects are large enough to satisfy such requirements.

In addition to cost, there are a few other drawbacks to custom wallcoverings. Most take a minimum of six weeks—usually longer—to be formulated and run. Before running the entire job, the manufacturer will provide *strike offs*, which are small printed samples, for the designer's review and approval. This gives the designer the opportunity to make color corrections or adjustments in the design, which, naturally, add time to the project schedule. If additional yardage is required at a later time—either for repairs or to accommodate renovation or expansion—the entire custom process, including time, yardage, and cost requirements, will be incurred again. To prevent this, it is recommended that such needs be taken into account and factored into the first run.

While custom wallcoverings can meet a project's special requirements, they must be properly planned, scheduled, and budgeted. The results can be extremely satisfying.

SPECIAL WALLCOVERING PRODUCTS

There is another type of wallcovering that is essentially a cross between wallcovering and wall paneling. Embossed with highly intricate designs, the most popular of these relatively thick wallcoverings are marketed under the trade names of *Lincrusta* and *Anaglypta*, which have been used since these products were first introduced in the late 1800s.

While Lincrusta is similar to a light-gauge linoleum, Anaglypta is made from either vinyl- or cellulose-based materials. These products are manufactured in rolls, panels, and narrow rolls for borders and trims. They are usually sold in their material's natural finish, and are intended to be painted. Many of the designs are derived from traditional patterns, though contemporary designs are also available. Regardless of pattern or materials, this type of wallcovering can be a definite advantage in situations where relief patterns are desirable and cost is a factor.

Although they are significantly heavier and thicker than standard vinyl wallcoverings, their level of flexibility and installation methods are very similar. Depending on their thickness and weight, they are installed with a thick, pastelike adhesive that is similar in texture to trowel-on flooring and made especially for this purpose.

MEASURING AND INSTALLATION

Although the task of measuring the space will, in most cases, be done by the contractor, the designer must know how much wallcovering is required for the project in order to produce an accurate cost estimate. The designer should ask the contractor to measure the space for two reasons. First, after inspecting the job site or drawings and specifications, the contractor, as a licensed professional, is in the best position to determine exactly how much wallcovering is required. Second, this places the burden of liability on the contractor; if the designer measures the space and makes an error, then he or she is responsible for any costs that might be incurred as a result.

On the other hand, it should be noted that the basic steps involved in measuring and estimating a space for wallcovering are not difficult, but they do require reasonable care on the part of the designer.

1. Measure the room's length, width, and height. Then add up the lengths and widths to determine the room's perimeter.

2. To calculate the room's total surface area, divide the perimeter by the width of the wallcovering, rounded up to the nearest whole number. The result is the number of lengths of wallcovering that will be required.

3. To determine the running length of wallcovering that will be required (which is normally given in linear yards), multiply the result by the wall height. If the wallcovering is patterned, first add the *match length*, or the measurement of space in which the pattern repeat is contained (indicated in the sample book), to the room's overall height.

As with measuring, the designer should be aware of basic hanging procedures even though the wallcovering will be hung by the contractor. This will enable him or her to correctly specify the method and to anticipate potential problems. If walls are damaged, they must be filled, smoothed, sanded, and sized with a glue solution. In extreme cases, they are then covered with a liner of heavy kraft paper made specifically for this purpose before the covering is hung. Most manufacturers can provide designers with their recommended wall preparation and installation procedures. Also, a day spent as a contractor's assistant will give a designer great insight into how wallcoverings are installed.

CARE AND MAINTENANCE

If a wallcovering is regularly maintained according to the manufacturer's recommended cleaning procedures, it will retain its newly installed look for many years. The designer may request in the specifications that the contractor supply the client with this information. If the designer is aware of how a wallcovering should be cared for and ensures that the client has been informed about these recommendations, many problems can be avoided.

Wallcoverings are an important part of what a commercial interior designer can provide for his or her clients. If the designer properly researches and correctly specifies the wallcoverings, and the client realizes what his or her responsibilities are, the installed product will meet the expectations of both, and satisfy the client for years to come.

WALLCOVERING SURFACE PREPARATION					
TYPE OF SUBSURFACE	STEP 1	STEP 2	STEP 3	STEP 4	STEP 5
FLAT OIL OR LATEX PAINT	WASH AND RINSE	APPLY WALL SIZING	HANG WITH ADHESIVE		
GLOSS OR SEMIGLOSS PAINT	WASH AND RINSE	APPLY WALL SIZING	HANG WITH ADHESIVE		
SAND FINISH OR TEXTURE	WASH AND RINSE	APPLY WALL SIZING	REGULAR LINING PAPER	HANG WITH ADHESIVE	
NEW DRYWALL	TAPE SEAMS AND NAIL HEADS	SAND SEAMS AND NAIL HEADS	APPLY WALL SIZING	HANG WITH ADHESIVE	
OLD WALLPAPER	REMOVE	WASH AND RINSE	APPLY WALL SIZING	HANG WITH ADHESIVE	
REMOVABLE VINYL WALLCOVERING	REMOVE	WASH AND RINSE	APPLY WALL SIZING	HANG WITH ADHESIVE	
VINYL WALLCOVERING THAT CANNOT BE REMOVED	WASH AND RINSE	APPLY WALL SIZING	HANG WITH ADHESIVE		
BORDERS OVER WALLCOVERING	WASH AND RINSE	APPLY WALL SIZING	HANG WITH ADHESIVE		
FOIL WALLCOVERING THAT CANNOT BE REMOVED	WASH AND BE RINSE	APPLY WALL SIZING	HANG WITH ADHESIVE		
BARE METAL	CLEAN	METAL PRIMER	APPLY WALL SIZING	HANG WITH ADHESIVE	
CEMENT OR CINDER BLOCK	CLEAN WITH WIRE BRUSH	APPLY WALL SIZING	UNDERCOVER	HANG WITH ADHESIVE	
WOOD PANELING	REMOVE WAX OR POLISH RESIDUE	RINSE	APPLY WALL SIZING	UNDERCOVER (HANG HORIZONTALLY)	HANG WITH ADHESIVE
MILDEW-STAINED SURFACE	WASH WITH BLEACH OR OTHER MILDEWCIDE	APPLY WALL SIZING	HANG WITH ADHESIVE		
SOURCE: GENON CORPORATION					

11

CEILING

MATERIALS

AND

FINISHES

IN THIS RECEPTION AREA, PERFORATED METAL CEILING TILES ARE USED TO HIGHLIGHT THE CENTRAL SEATING ARRANGEMENT AND COMPLEMENT THE STEPPED TEGULAR-EDGED TILES AND MARBLE GRID ACCENTS. (REFER ALSO TO THE SECTION ON "SPECIAL CEILING MATERIALS AND TREATMENTS," LATER IN THIS CHAPTER.) *PHOTO BY THE MAKERS OF ARMSTRONG CEILING SYSTEMS*

In view of the fact that the ceilings of the first shelters consisted merely of the underside of whatever kept the elements out, it is probably safe to assume that their design was given little or no conscious thought. Since that time, whatever defines the interior space overhead has been dealt with by architects and designers in one of two ways: by either exposing and embellishing the structure beneath the roof, or by hiding it. The beautiful exposed wood beams of the great halls of English castles and stone arches of Romanesque and Gothic cathedrals show how the medieval Europeans used the structural elements of their buildings to enhance the beauty of the interior space. To conceal a Gothic cathedral's substructure, architects either filled in the stone ceiling with brick and covered it with a wooden trussed roof, or simply built a smaller, lighter roof just below the main one, creating a smooth surface that could be painted or otherwise decorated. Later, plaster was applied directly to the surfaces of vaulted ceilings, then elaborately ornamented. The seventeenth-century French styles of Louis XV, Louis XVI, and Rococo, whose complex ornamentation was limited only by the media, materials, and imaginations of the artisans of the period, are all excellent examples of this. Other ceiling forms combine elements of both approaches, such as the coffered ceiling, which alternates carved exposed beams with recessed plaster surfaces in the spaces between.

TYPES OF CEILINGS

While modern interior designers are still faced with basically the same two approaches to ceilings—expose or hide—they must concern themselves with those elements that require space above the ceiling, including air ducts, air control boxes, electrical conduits, fire proofing, lighting, and sprinkler systems, not to mention the substructure of the building itself. In most cases, buildings constructed before the twentieth century did not need to incorporate any of these kinds of elements, which from the first were not intended to be exposed. As a result, most ceiling types currently in use enclose rather than reveal the structure and its accompanying hardware.

There are three ways in which a ceiling can be attached to the horizontal elements of the substructure, which usually consist of either wood joists or steel beams. The method used depends on their design and interval of spacing. (See also Chapter 1, "Interior Substructures: Floors, Walls, and Ceilings" for more information.)

ATTACHED CEILINGS

In an attached ceiling, which is also referred to as *direct installation*, the material of the ceiling is affixed directly to the underside of the roof or the structure of the floor above. It can be fastened mechanically, with nails or bolts, or by using an adhesive or mastic. The installation of this type of ceiling is complicated—or may even be ruled out completely—if the surface of the substructure is irregular.

FURRED CEILINGS

The furred ceiling, which is also known as *semidirect installation*, solves the problem of irregular surfaces. The ceiling material is installed with *furring strips*, which are small linear pieces of wood or metal that are wired or attached to the structure above. Wood furring strips are usually about 1 × 2 inches nominally. Metal furring strips (also known as *hat channels)*, which are made from thin-gauge metal, are used to span irregular surfaces or spaces between structural members.

SUSPENDED CEILINGS

In view of the number of elements that require space above the ceiling, which make it difficult if not impossible to successfully create a level surface with either direct or semidirect installation, it's little wonder that the suspended ceiling is the most common in contract interiors today.

Essentially, the suspended ceiling takes the basic furring grid and suspends it below the elements that need to be covered. It allows the ceiling to be installed at almost any height, as long as the hardware above has sufficient room. For instance, if the structure of the roof or floor above is 18 feet above the floor, and the various hardware and systems are 15 feet above the floor, the ceiling can easily be installed at a height of 10 feet. In addition, special shapes, angles, and soffits can be created by merely hanging the grid at an angle or by wiring the special shape into position. Finally, this type of ceiling can easily accommodate the variety of items that must penetrate the ceiling surface, providing a platform of sorts for lights and air diffusers. While there are several varieties of suspended ceiling, their single identifying characteristic is the *suspension grid*, which is what is actually hung from the structure above it.

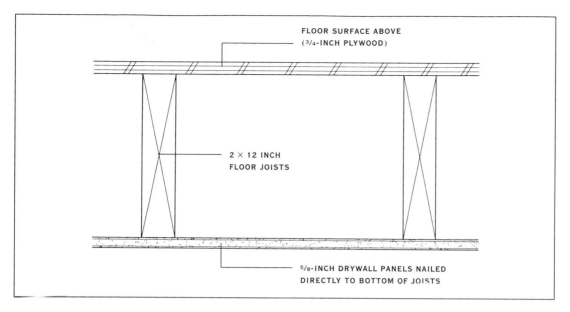

FLOOR SURFACE ABOVE
(3/4-INCH PLYWOOD)

2 × 12 INCH
FLOOR JOISTS

5/8-INCH DRYWALL PANELS NAILED
DIRECTLY TO BOTTOM OF JOISTS

CROSS-SECTION
DRAWINGS OF AN
ATTACHED CEILING,
OR A DIRECT
INSTALLATION *(TOP)*,
A FURRED CEILING,
OR A SEMIDIRECT
INSTALLATION
(CENTER), AND A
SUSPENDED CEILING
(BOTTOM).

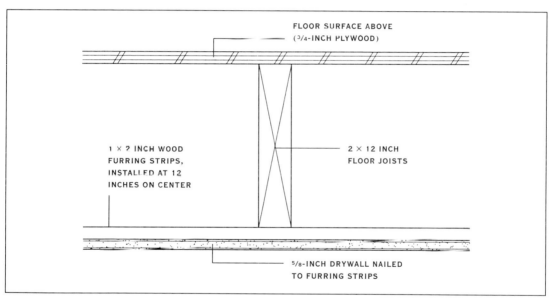

FLOOR SURFACE ABOVE
(3/4-INCH PLYWOOD)

1 × 2 INCH WOOD
FURRING STRIPS,
INSTALLED AT 12
INCHES ON CENTER

2 × 12 INCH
FLOOR JOISTS

5/8-INCH DRYWALL NAILED
TO FURRING STRIPS

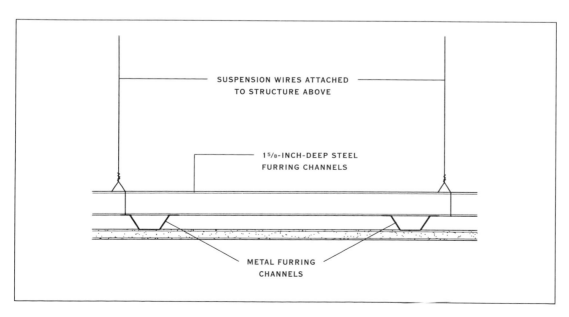

SUSPENSION WIRES ATTACHED
TO STRUCTURE ABOVE

1 5/8-INCH-DEEP STEEL
FURRING CHANNELS

METAL FURRING
CHANNELS

One form of grid, which is constructed to support drywall panels, uses steel tie wires to suspend a series of $1^5/8$-inch-deep steel channels from the structure above. Depending on the elements above and the ceiling material used, these channels are spaced from 16 to 24 inches apart. Metal furring channels are then attached to the steel channels with wire furring clips, creating the grid. Metal lath (for plaster) or drywall panels are then wired or screwed to the bottoms of the metal furring channels. For a plaster finish the various coats are applied, and for drywall the joints are taped, mudded, and sanded, in the same manner as for a wall surface. In both cases the final result is a flat, level surface ready for paint, wallcovering, or practically any other finish material.

Suspended ceiling systems are also manufactured to support preformed panels or tiles, which makes installation and access to any overhead equipment in need of service relatively easy. In the *T-bar system* (whose name is derived from the intersection of its grid members), the grid consists of specially shaped metal strips that are available in 20-, 4-, and 2-foot lengths approximately $1^1/2$ inches deep and $^{15}/16$ inch wide. These strips, which are usually finished in a flat or low-luster off-white paint, are perforated with small holes and slots to increase the number of installation configurations. Two of the most common grid configurations are 2×4 feet and 2×2 feet. The installation of this system is quite simple. An angle is attached to the wall where the ceiling and the wall will meet. The installer uses a rotating laser beam device whose light ray is set to correspond with the intended ceiling height to mark a line on the walls at the appropriate point around the entire space. This ensures that the installation of the support angles—and, therefore, the ceiling—is level and flat.

For 2×4 grid ceilings, the installer then connects the T-bars to the wall angles, spacing them at 4-foot intervals. Then the 4-foot bars are placed perpendicular to the T-bars, and attached to one another with fastening tabs that are fitted into small holes in the upper portion of the bar. A second set of 4-foot bars is then installed at 2-foot intervals, creating the 2×4 grid. For a 2×2 grid, a set of 2-foot-long T-bars are attached to the structure above with medium-gauge wires, where they are either shot into a floor slab with small explosive charges or wrapped securely around the building structure. Local building codes usually specify the gauge of wire and the number of times the wire must be turned and wrapped around itself.

OTHER SUSPENDED CEILING SYSTEMS

Although the T-bar grid described above is the most common, suspended ceiling systems are available in a variety of configurations. Recently, a lighter, more delicate-looking version of the T-bar, about $^9/16$ inch wide, has become quite popular. Another new shape shifts the visual emphasis toward the grid by means of a reveal that is the result of a small slot at the bottom of the T, offering designers a more sophisticated look. Other options and variations are available. In addition to the standard white or off-white, many grids are manufactured in a range of neutral colors; special colors can be ordered if the minimum quantity required is met. Some manufacturers offer metallic finishes such as brass, chrome, or copper.

It is not always necessary for the grid to be visible. One type of *concealed grid system* called the *Z-spline* uses hardware called *Z clips* that slide into slots in the edge of the ceiling tile. When the tiles are installed, they essentially hide the grid, leaving only a thin joint visible between them. Another type of concealed grid snaps the tiles into recessed slots in the edges with small clips. A small knifelike tool is used to remove the tile to gain access to any systems above.

THE T-BAR SUSPENSION GRID IS AVAILABLE IN SEVERAL CONFIGURATIONS AND CAN BE FITTED WITH A WIDE VARIETY OF PANELS OR TILES *(FROM TOP LEFT TO BOTTOM RIGHT)*: A BASIC WHITE T-BAR GRID PAIRED WITH A REVEAL-STYLE TILE; A ⁹/₁₆-INCH T-BAR GRID WITH A GROOVED TILE; A REVEAL T-BAR GRID WITH A HEAVILY TEXTURED TILE; AND A ROUNDED T-BAR GRID WITH A BEVELED TEGULAR-EDGED TILE. (SEE ALSO "SPECIAL CEILING MATERIALS AND TREATMENTS," LATER IN THIS CHAPTER.) *PHOTOS BY THE MAKERS OF ARMSTRONG CEILING SYSTEMS*

Several specialty grids and accessories are also available. Fire-rated grids, which conform to testing specifications conducted by independent laboratories, are manufactured with a heavier-gauge steel. If the building code requires it, retention and impact clips are available to hold the ceiling tiles in the grid. All these items give the suspension system a versatility that was unavailable until recently.

SUSPENDED CEILING SYSTEM PANELS

In addition to plaster and drywall, which are used in standard suspension systems, there are two general categories of ceiling panels available to the interior designer: cellulose- or wood fiber–based, and mineral wool–based.

The cellulose-based products are lightweight and reasonably economical. They are manufactured from small wood chips that have been sorted to limit their size and washed to remove surface impurities. The chips are then fed into a refiner, which reduces them to pulp. Water is alternately added and extracted several times as the pulp is refined and densifies. Lime is added to control the pH, and alum is added to help to stabilize the mixture. The refined pulp mixture is then pumped into a forming machine. The water is extracted and the fibers are arranged in several directions to increase strength. The material is pressed into a uniform thickness, cut, and run through a series of driers. During the finishing process, one side of the tile is sanded to a smooth surface, then painted with primer. Depending on the product, the tile is then either ironed smooth or embossed with any of a variety of patterns, from random to highly regular, from shallow to deep, and cut to its final size. (Special shapes and/or edge treatments are also cut into the tile at this point.) Following a final coat of flat paint, some tiles are then perforated with holes, whose size depends on the product's intended final texture and acoustical properties. The finished tiles are then wrapped for shipping.

BOTH CELLULOSE-BASED AND MINERAL WOOL–BASED CEILING TILES ARE MANUFACTURED IN A RANGE OF SIZES AND TEXTURES *(LEFT)*. THEY CAN ALSO BE CUT OR ROUTED TO SIMULATE SMALLER TILE CONFIGURATIONS *(RIGHT)*. *PHOTOS BY THE MAKERS OF ARMSTRONG CEILING SYSTEMS*

Mineral wool–based products are manufactured in a similar manner. The wool is added to a wet binder of starch, kraft paper, and clay and mixed until thoroughly blended. The resulting slurry is pumped into a tank and dispensed onto a forming wire at a steady rate. The excess binding solution is drained away and the remaining material is cut into 52-inch squares and dried. The panels are then cut to final size and cast or embossed to create textures or cut with special edge shapes and painted. Finally, after the paint has cured, the panels are packaged for shipping.

SPECIAL INSTALLATION REQUIREMENTS

Regardless of which suspension system or grid is used, it must be installed to withstand the force of an earthquake. It is not difficult to imagine the danger that would confront building occupants as ceiling tiles, lights, and heating and ventilation equipment fell out of the grid if it should fail. The interior designer must consult the building code and local authorities to determine the exact requirements for each municipality.

Most building codes require that three elements be used to support the ceiling grid. First, vertical *hanger wires*, which actually hold the ceiling up, are installed at 4-foot intervals on center in each direction. Second, four wires (one in each direction) must be attached to each channel at 10-foot intervals on center at a 45-degree angle, and each wire must be 90 degrees to another angled wire. This configuration helps to prevent the ceiling from buckling when subjected to the horizontal force of a tremor. Third, a metal strut must be securely fastened at 10-foot intervals on center to both the building structure or floor above and the grid below, which prevents damage as a result of a tremor's vertical forces.

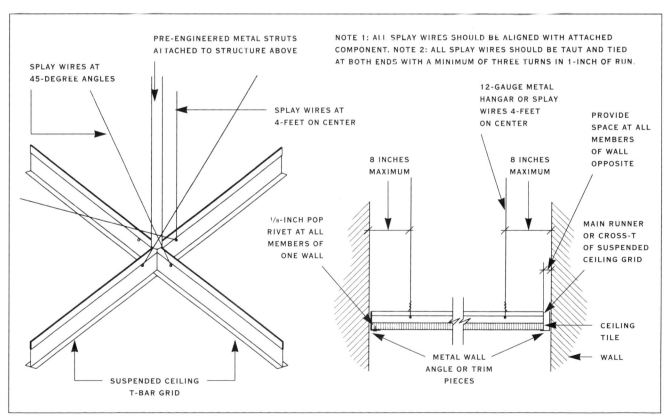

THESE SPECIFICATION DRAWINGS DETAIL A SUSPENDED CEILING INSTALLATION'S SEISMIC REQUIREMENTS.

SPECIAL CEILING MATERIALS AND TREATMENTS

Since the early 1980s, the interior design community and its clientele have demanded more variety in their ceiling finishes. While plaster can be shaped into curves, columns, and various trims and moldings—and, in fact, plaster decoration has recently experienced a moderate resurgence—the use of plaster and drywall for ceilings is essentially limited to flat surfaces to which texture can then be applied. The plaster, which is mixed (or premixed) to a thick, smooth consistency, is troweled onto the surface of the ceiling, and the desired texture is then carefully smoothed or swirled into it. For an inexpensive, uniformly rough texture, a slightly lumpy cellulose-water-binder mixture can be sprayed onto a plaster or drywall ceiling.

The somewhat limited, repetitive scheme of the suspended ceiling system's grid challenges interior designers to create unique ceiling looks. Before considering a custom grid system, however, a designer should carefully investigate a manufacturer's standard product line for possible points of departure. It should also be noted that almost any material that can be cut into a 2-foot module and falls below a certain weight maximum can be incorporated into the grid.

For example, one of the easiest modifications of a standard ceiling for a manufacturer to fabricate is the *tegular-edged tile.* This special treatment is created by cutting away a portion of the tile edge at an angle, which allows the tile to extend down from the grid about $3/8$ inch. By emphasizing the grid and hiding any uneven areas in the ceiling, this variation creates a more formal look without a significant increase in cost. Tegular tile edges can also be beveled, stepped, or rounded, for a somewhat softer look.

A variation on the tegular edge modifies the entire face of the tile. For example, a $3/8$-inch edge treatment can be repeated in a 1-inch groove (or series of grooves) across the face. Depending on the location and number of cuts, this treatment can be used to simulate 2×2 or 1×1 foot tiles. In another variation, the grooves are made even narrower and closer together, creating a subgrid within a 2-foot-square module of 6-inch or even 1-inch squares.

CROSS-SECTION DRAWINGS THAT COMPARE THE INSTALLATION OF A STANDARD CEILING TILE (*TOP LEFT*) WITH REVEAL, RADIUS, AND STEPPED TEGULAR-EDGED TILES.

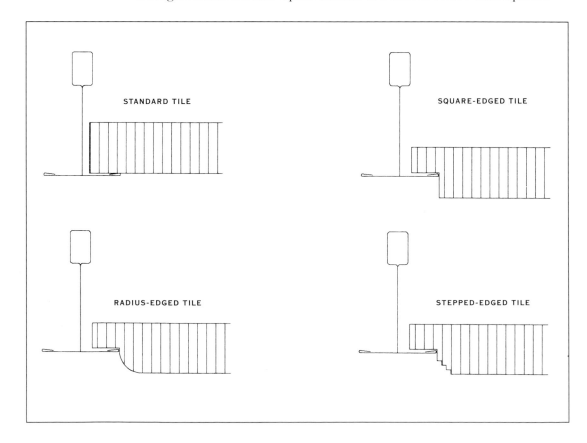

STANDARD TILE

SQUARE-EDGED TILE

RADIUS-EDGED TILE

STEPPED-EDGED TILE

Another recent development involves routing a shape into the tile face. The eight or ten cuts that are available are not all regular or symmetrical, so the designer can orient and position the tiles for a provocative random configuration.

For another formal look, most manufacturers offer a line of *grid accents*, which are beveled 2-inch or 3½-inch plastic squares that are used to emphasize tile corners. This element, which is used in conjunction with specially designed ceiling tiles, is turned at a 45-degree angle to the grid and placed at specific grid intersections. Grid accents, which are available in a variety of colors and patterns, can lend a decorative feel to what would otherwise be a standard suspended ceiling.

By covering or wrapping standard cellulose- or mineral wool–based tiles, their somewhat limited looks and relatively dent-prone surfaces can be altered for either decorative or utilitarian purposes. Consider, for example, a high-moisture and high-traffic location such as a swimming pool or restaurant kitchen. Neither of the standard tile types perform well or remain stable in the presence of moisture or humidity, which also means that they cannot be cleaned with alkaline cleaning solutions. One manufacturer addresses this problem by coating one of its products with a dense ceramic material, strengthening the tile and increasing its resistance to moisture, dirt, and grease. Another manufacturer coats its tile with a tough polymeric finish. Still another offers a product clad with a vinyl-faced aluminum that is highly resistant to dirt, grease, and chlorine fumes. Mylar-clad tiles are ideal in environments where cleanliness is a priority, such as hospitals and computer cleanrooms. For increased durability, tiles are covered with metal or manufactured with tough epoxylike binders, making them suitable for use in public schools and detention facilities. These products usually also enjoy an increased fire rating as a result of their supplemental materials, giving designers more choices in situations that require it.

WITH THE VARIETY OF TILES AND PANELS AVAILABLE, A RANGE OF CEILING TREATMENTS IS POSSIBLE: ROUTED TILES ARE ARRANGED TO CREATE A CURVILINEAR CEILING DESIGN IN A COCKTAIL LOUNGE *(LEFT)*, AND SMOOTH WHITE GRID ACCENTS ARE USED TO CONTRAST WITH OFF-WHITE TEXTURED PANELS *(ABOVE)*. *PHOTOS BY THE MAKERS OF ARMSTRONG CEILING SYSTEMS*

As mentioned above, tiles are also wrapped or covered for aesthetic reasons. Many companies produce fabric-wrapped tiles, whose softer looks and range of colors and patterns are simply not available in standard tile lines. Their main disadvantage is that they cannot be easily cleaned, and so should not be chosen for sites where dirt is a problem.

The materials that make up a tile can also be varied. One commmon reason, among others, is for sound control. While most standard ceiling tiles have a reasonable acoustical rating, a fiberglass tile absorbs significantly more sound than its standard counterparts. Fiberglass tiles were designed specifically for large, open office spaces, where sound control is imperative. They are composed of a lighter resin-impregnated fiberglass to prevent them from sagging, and are faced with either painted cloth or perforated vinyl.

As with wrapped or covered tiles, ceiling tile materials can be changed completely to add excitement to a space and improve the overall look of a project. By choosing the proper finish and employing grain-matching techniques, shaped, edged, or cut tiles of nearly any species of wood, either solid or veneered, as well as plywood, can be used to create a stunning ceiling treatment. When used with a suitable backing, wood strips can be aligned linearly for a "grille" ceiling or overlapped to make an "egg crate" design. The main obstacle to using wood in a ceiling treatment is its weight. If care is taken to ensure that the suspension system can carry any additional weight, this potential problem can be avoided.

ANOTHER SUSPENDED CEILING VARIATION: TILES WRAPPED WITH FABRIC FOR A SOFT LOOK. *PHOTO BY THE MAKERS OF ARMSTRONG CEILING SYSTEMS*

FIBERGLASS TILES ARE USED PRIMARILY TO CONTROL SOUND IN LARGE, OPEN SPACES. *PHOTO BY THE MAKERS OF ARMSTRONG CEILING SYSTEMS*

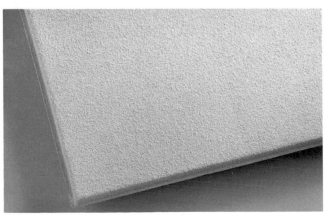

In addition to their use in the suspension grid, metals are also used in other ceiling applications. In one contemporary treatment, which is available in a wide range of painted finishes as well as in standard anodized and polished versions, long strips of preformed aluminum are attached with brackets to a special grid. Embossed or perforated metal panels are made to fit into a standard 2 × 2 foot T-bar grid. Some manufacturers also offer reproductions of tinplate ceilings that were popular at the turn of the twentieth century.

Many architects and interior designers feel that whatever systems and structures are usually hidden above a ceiling are functional elements that relate to the integrity of a space and should be left exposed. In some ceiling treatments, the air ducts on heating and ventilation systems are painted to add an element of contrast. A designer also has the option of painting the ceiling structure and all of the exposed equipment a flat black, de-emphasizing it visually and making it virtually "disappear." This treatment, which creates the illusion of smoked glass, is only successful if *everything* is painted black and no lights are pointed upward or installed above the grid.

As one can see, the lowly (or lofty) ceiling can become an exciting design element, even on a strict budget. A designer need only identify potential problems and attempt to address them in his or her treatment. The results can be surprising as well as satisfying.

SUSPENDED CEILING SYSTEMS MANUFACTURERS ALSO INCORPORATE SUCH SPECIAL MATERIALS AS WOOD AND METAL INTO THEIR PRODUCT LINES. *PHOTOS BY THE MAKERS OF ARMSTRONG CEILING SYSTEMS*

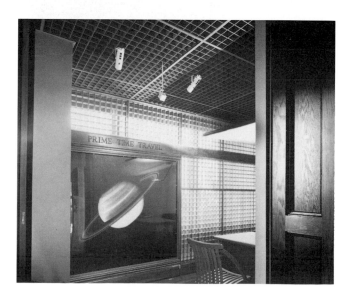

12

FURNITURE

THE OPEN OFFICE THAT IS DIVIDED INTO SMALLER SPACES WITH SYSTEM FURNITURE UNITS IS ONE OF THE MOST COMMON LARGE OFFICE CONFIGURATIONS IN USE TODAY. *COURTESY OF HERMAN MILLER, INC.*

The first furniture consisted of simple chests that were used for both seating and storage. Embellished with color, texture, drawings, and carvings, the furnishings of the ruling classes were for some time the only household appointments that were viewed as objects of comfort, beauty, originality, and status. Compared with its rather rudimentary origins, furniture today is highly specialized and refined. It is also available to more people, in a much greater variety of styles, and fulfills a wider range of uses than ever before. In many ways, however, the basic goal of furniture has remained the same: To make human existence somewhat more comfortable while suiting individual tastes and appealing to an aesthetic sensibility. The primary purpose of furniture, regardless of type, is the satisfaction of a specific function.

Interior designers must always be on the alert for new products that might help meet their clients' needs or solve a problem concerning space: New materials, combinations of materials, and materials used in a new ways are continually developed and sought after for these reasons. Furniture's current role in contract interior design is such that clients and designers alike consider it first and foremost among the elements contained within a space. This chapter deals with a single aspect of furniture: its use within and relationship to a particular space.

FREESTANDING FURNITURE

Freestanding furniture, which is manufactured to general standards and in reasonably large quantities—that is, it can be ordered from a manufacturer's catalog—and can be placed, within reason, wherever it is desired, is the most widely available furniture type. Much of the furniture specified by contract interior designers is freestanding, and its popularity reflects the needs of most commercial clients. For instance, businesses are a great deal more mobile today than ever before, and are likely to move to suit their physical needs, whether to larger offices as they grow and expand, or to smaller space if downsizing has occurred; freestanding furniture can be easily moved with them. Clients also value flexibility: If a meeting in a conference room requires additional seating, for example, chairs from an adjoining conference room or office can be moved in temporarily to accommodate the meeting. If more table space is required, two tables can be pushed together. If a particular department requires more staff members, desks, chairs, and files can be moved from other locations or purchased to fulfill that need. The only limitation to freestanding furniture is size: There must be room for the particular piece or arrangement of pieces so that they can be used as the client and designer intended.

MATERIALS

There are four main categories of materials that are used in the manufacture of freestanding furniture: wood, metal, plastic, and fabric. In most instances, freestanding furniture specifically designed for use in contract interiors is a synthesis of all four of these categories.

WOOD

Used by artisans to create furniture for centuries, wood is still one of the primary materials used to fabricate freestanding furniture. Although wood is not as plentiful as it once was, and furniture is now made from a variety of materials, when most people think of a desk or a table, they probably picture one made from wood. The reasons for wood's continuing popularity have not changed: Wood is a beautiful material whose color variations and grain patterns seem to impart a warmth and comfortable feeling both to the piece itself and the space. With the wide range of tools available to manufacturers today, the workability of specific varieties of wood is not as important as it once was. Regardless of the means of fabrication, a beautifully shaped or carved piece of furniture is a joy to look at.

METAL

Metal is another material that is used in the manufacture of furniture. The most common metals used to make furniture include iron, steel, aluminum, and brass. Metal was first used to make furniture hardware—hinges, latches, and handles—an enterprise to which it was well suited, as hardware is by nature subject to more wear than the rest of a piece of furniture because of movement and abrasion. Early furniture hardware was made by hand, one piece at a time. With the advent of mass-production techniques, metal became much easier to fabricate. As a result, it was soon used to make other types of furniture hardware such as drawer glides, braces, and supports.

Metal was first incorporated as a major element in furniture in the early twentieth century. When all-metal furniture was introduced in the 1930s, it seemed utilitarian and was generally cheap- and awkward-looking. Most people remember the heavy gray metal desks that have now been relegated to a workroom or storage room: The emphasis seems to have been placed on economy rather than on design or aesthetics.

Today, metal is synonymous with quality and durability. New techniques in shaping, texturing, and painting metal surfaces have made most metal furniture as aesthetically inviting as wood furniture. In fact, many companies manufacture furniture made almost entirely of metal. The most successful companies do not compete with traditional manufacturers by attempting to duplicate wood designs. Their furniture has an appealing modern look, exemplified by clean lines and simple shapes.

PLASTIC

A relatively new material, synthetic plastic was developed in the early twentieth century. Plastic is created chemically and has a variety of properties; the most signficant and relevant to furniture manufacture is that it can be molded into almost any shape. This helps furniture designers fabricate special shapes for specific parts of a piece or even an entire piece. Another important property of plastic is its ability to be successfully produced in almost any color, which gives the designer more latitude in blending his or her furniture designs with other elements within a space. Because of these properties, plastic can be made to look like many other materials, usually at a lower cost.

Plastic can also be made to almost any degree of hardness, making it appropriate for a number of applications, which gives designers and manufacturers a range of options: Furniture can be either hard and durable or soft and comfortable, depending on its intended use. Another important characteristic of plastic is that it is usually much lighter, yet still as strong, or possibly stronger, than other furniture materials. The sum of these characteristics amounts to a useful and versatile material.

As with most materials, however, there are drawbacks. Plastic tends to look sterile, and, in some cases, simply uninviting, criticisms that are usually voiced by designers who prefer to work with natural materials. But as plastic is used more often and manufacturing techniques continue to improve, its varieties and the ways it can be used in furniture construction will increase, as will our familiarity and comfort level with it. This material will become even more important to designers and consumers alike as the world's natural resources continue to be depleted.

FABRICS

The choice of upholstery fabrics is almost limitless. The range of designs, weaves, textures, and colors available is one of the most exciting design factors for the interior designer and the public. Upholstery fabrics can change the appearance of furniture, and, more than any other element in an interior, can provide color accent and create the total mood and atmosphere of a space. Because of this, fabrics must be carefully specified; the wrong fabric can be detrimental to an otherwise carefully planned space. Fabrics that are not meant for heavy-duty use may quickly become worn. Other fabrics can easily become dirty, and even the wrong color selection can cause maintenance difficulties.

Durability is an important quality expected from upholstery fabrics. One of the key factors in fabric wear is abrasion. The areas that receive the most abrasion on upholstered pieces always show wear first. Results from abrasion resistance testing are available and may be requested from the manufacturer. Abrasion may also cause loss of color if the dye has not properly penetrated the fabric. It is important, however, that life expectancy not be the only criterion considered when selecting and specifying fabrics; appearance, feel, and other comfort considerations should not be overlooked.

Specification of fabrics requires a fair amount of knowledge about textiles and, above all, requires the understanding that the counsel of experts may need to be sought. Reputable manufacturers usually label their fabrics clearly with fiber content and special features or treatment. If this is not done, the pertinent information should be obtained from the manufacturer.

COMPONENTS

Because most furniture is designed to fill a specific function—particularly that used in commercial interiors—the style, materials, and intended use of freestanding components are as varied and numerous as the clients who use them. With a focus on the pieces that are most commonly used in contract interiors, the following is an evaluation of the major components of freestanding furniture and the function that each is intended to perform.

CHAIRS

Probably the most common freestanding component, chairs are made to handle a wide range of work situations. Most task-specific and secretarial chairs have adjustable height and back mechanisms to ensure that the user receives maximum comfort. A variation on the basic office chair is the executive chair, which usually has a higher back and may have fewer adjustment options. Executive chairs are more comfortable than standard office chairs, yet still provide adequate support. For situations that require comfort with only occasional use, other types of chairs are available. One example is an office guest chair, which usually has no adjustments and may have either legs or a sled base. The conference chair is normally positioned on casters with a base that swivels and tilts, which enable its occupant to shift and move. Since the discussion at hand is the most important element within a conference room, a conference chair should be comfortable, but not comfortable enough to put its occupant to sleep.

A STANDARD TASK CHAIR WITH ADJUSTABLE BACK AND HEIGHT MECHANISMS *(NEAR RIGHT)* AND THE SLED BASE CHAIR, WHICH IS INTENDED PRIMARILY FOR OFFICE GUESTS *(FAR RIGHT). COURTESY OF HERMAN MILLER, INC.*

Stacking or folding chairs, which are designed for occasional use and subsequent storage, are used when a high degree of flexibility is necessary. They are usually less expensive than the chairs described above but are still reasonably comfortable.

While there is a surprising range in the quality of furnishings used in reception or waiting areas, both image and comfort are considered when a choice is made. Opulent corporate reception areas reflect the company's desire to portray an image of success. In some professional settings, such as doctors' or dentists' offices, comfort and image in a waiting room take a backseat to the number of people that must be accommodated on an average workday.

Although benches, stools, sofas, and other seating appointments are not as common as chairs in contract interiors, they are important elements in such spaces as executive offices as well as some reception areas.

A SET OF STACKING CHAIRS *(LEFT)* AND A LEATHER SOFA *(BELOW)*, WHICH WOULD BE USED IN A RECEPTION AREA OR EXECUTIVE OFFICE. *COURTESY OF HERMAN MILLER, INC.*

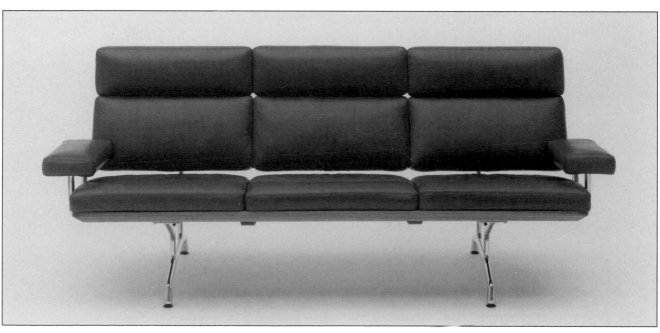

DESKS

The primary item in an office workspace—almost as common as a chair—a desk is a horizontal worksurface usually accompanied by a variety of storage drawers that contain files and work supplies. The size and configuration of the drawers may vary, but their main purpose is to aid the occupant by organizing and storing work-related materials.

There are several other items that are directly related to the desk. For example, the return, which is normally attached to the desk at a 90-degree angle, is used for the typewriter or computer, leaving the main desk surface free for paperwork and other tasks. To accommodate the thickness of the typewriter keyboard comfortably, the height of the return is usually about 2 to 4 inches lower than the surface of the main desk area. However, with the increased popularity of computers, which usually have relatively thin keyboards, a lower height for the return has become less important. In fact, many people now prefer the desk and the return to be the same height. Another result of the computer's widespread use, the typewriter is now commonly relegated to a specialized desk.

When computers are used by several people for short periods of time, special single-unit desks can accommodate all of the computer's elements—keyboard, hard drive, monitor, printer, and so on—and usually require far less space than standard desks. For workers who sort and organize paperwork, there are desks whose storage or sorting bins are positioned directly above the main worksurface.

The sizes of most desks usually conform to a rough standard. Obviously, larger desks are not necessarily bestowed on those with the most work; the size of desk has a great deal to do with a person's title and his or her position within a company. Often larger or more formal desks will be accompanied by a credenza, which is usually detached from the desk and placed directly behind it. Credenzas have a variety of doors and drawers for storage, as well as one or more three-to-four shelf bookcase units that are designed to rest on top. The bookcase unit is commonly used in executive offices.

It is probably safe to say that desks are made to fit almost every work situation. Regardless of its configuration, the desk is an essential element of the current commercial work environment.

THIS FREESTANDING DESK FEATURES A TYPEWRITER RETURN THAT IS A FEW INCHES LOWER THAN THE MAIN WORKSURFACE. *COURTESY OF HERMAN MILLER, INC.*

IN THIS EXECUTIVE'S
OFFICE, THE LARGE
ALL-WOOD DESK
IS COMPLEMENTED
BY A MATCHING
CREDENZA/BOOKCASE
COMBINATION AND
DRAFTING TABLE.
*COURTESY OF
HERMAN MILLER, INC.*

THESE WORKSTATIONS ARE DESIGNED TO ACCOMMODATE ALL OF THE NECESSARY COMPUTER COMPONENTS AND INCREASE THE COMFORT AND EFFICIENCY OF THE USER. *COURTESY OF HERMAN MILLER, INC.*

TABLES

In its simplest form, a table is a worksurface supported on legs whose size and design depend on the task it is intended to serve. Compared with the desk, the table probably has a greater variety of uses. In many cases, a table is used as a desk, with work supplies and files stored elsewhere.

In an executive office, a table used as a desk is much less imposing or intimidating than a full-sized desk. In a staff environment, the surface of the table can be used to collate, sort, or spread out mail, papers, books, and other work-related materials. Tables used for these kinds of tasks are not normally assigned to a particular employee, but are instead located in a common area and used temporarily on an as-needed basis. In addition, they are usually both inexpensive and durable.

One of the most common office uses for the table is in a conference room, where the participants in a meeting are able to face each other while seated, allowing for convenient communication. The surface of the table is used for note-taking, referring to handouts, or otherwise serving the needs of those who use the room.

ONE OF THE MORE COMMON OFFICE USES FOR THE TABLE IS IN THE CONFERENCE ROOM. *COURTESY OF HERMAN MILLER, INC.*

A SMALLER VERSION OF A CONFERENCE TABLE CAN BE USED IN A LARGE EXECUTIVE OFFICE. *COURTESY OF HERMAN MILLER, INC.*

FILING CABINETS
OF VARIOUS
SIZES, CABINETS,
CLOSETS, AND
ENCLOSED SHELVES
ARE ALL USED
FOR STORAGE IN
COMMERCIAL OFFICE
ENVIRONMENTS.
*COURTESY OF
HERMAN MILLER, INC.*

STORAGE

Though they are in some ways ancillary to the components discussed above, storage components are an important and necessary part of an office's furnishings. Storage components, which are designed to help workers accomplish their jobs efficiently, are available in a wide range of styles, from the most basic and functional to the latest in color and design.

Filing cabinets, bookcases, chests, and cabinets, each of which is used to store, organize, and easily access materials, all fall under the general category of storage. Filing cabinets are used to store records, which are then arranged so that they can easily be accessed and referred to. Bookcases contain books and other reading and research materials so that they can be easily located and used. Chests are primarily used to store materials and supplies, as well as bulky or unwieldy items that are needed relatively infrequently.

QUALITY

The consideration of quality for any piece of furniture is based on two attributes: construction and design. Because the perception of quality is in part a subjective judgment, it is easy to believe that the choice of furniture is based primarily on personal taste. However, the interior designer should strive to develop a standard of quality unrelated to his or her personal opinion, based on what is good and bad regarding both construction and design. While remaining open to the tastes of the client, the designer can then make a decision based primarily on the needs of the space, which will surely benefit all concerned.

When a designer chooses furniture for a project, he or she should be as concerned with functionality and durability as with appropriateness of design. Many projects that are impressive when first completed may lose their looks after a relatively short period of time as a result of unsuitable choices. The style or design of a piece, its scale in relation to the overall space and to the other pieces in the room, and its orientation are all important points to consider when designing a project. However, a highly developed sense of aesthetics is worth little when a functional aspect of a piece of furniture contributes to its failure. For instance, a client will very likely forget that he or she was thrilled with the design of a chair when its upholstery frays as a result of normal wear. Therefore, as part of the process of choosing and placing furniture, designers should make sure that they understand where and how a piece will be used.

Designers should be prepared to tactfully educate their clients when their tastes do not reflect the project's potential. On the other hand, designers should be tolerant of differing opinions concerning quality, and should take care not to impose their personal preferences on clients, particularly when they do not fit a program. Because a project's quality is also determined in part by the client's budget, designers should ask clients to inform them about their budget constraints and requirements as well.

STYLE

The study of the history of furniture design is fundamental to an interior designer's education. An awareness and understanding of what was done before assists designers in the practice their craft, both today and in the future.

Ornamentation—and its eventual absence from twentieth-century furniture—has been a consistent part of the evolution of the furniture craft; design and functionality are other important characteristics. The circumstances that contributed to a piece's style—where a piece of furniture was to be used, who was going to use it, the era during which it was designed, and the philosophy of the designer—continually competed for prominence. Designers' allusions to historical elements in their own work illustrate which design approaches were most successful; those that are no longer used simply remain a part of history.

In contract interior design, the functionality of furniture is, in most instances, the designer's primary consideration. In many areas of the world, the dominant mode of work has changed from manual labor to tasks that involve the movement and dissemination of information. This evolution of work means that the design of furniture intended for the workplace must respond to the needs of new tasks, and help workers accomplish them efficiently. Because the commercial office environment essentially did not exist until the late nineteenth century, the influences that created the furniture styles up to that point in time are completely different from those that are generally in use today. For example, a secretary's desk in the style of Louis XV would look ridiculous with a computer sitting on top of it.

Among others, the terms "formal," "casual," "traditional," "contemporary," and "modern" are all used to describe various styles of commercial office furniture, and the effects of its style are generally more subtle than those of residential or special-use furniture. In commercial furniture, the material from which a piece of furniture is made is generally more important than how it is shaped. For example, metal furniture makes a "modern" impression, while wood tends to impart a "traditional" feeling to a room. The type, color, and finish of wood used in a piece of furniture can also affect the mood of a space, and consequently, its style. Moldings around desk tops, simple designs and shapes along the legs, raised panels on vertical surfaces, and hardware can also affect the perceived style of a piece of wood furniture.

Generally, finish elements such as wallcoverings, paint, carpeting, and artwork do more to set the scene for the "style" of a space than the furniture, which should simply complement it. Today's contract interior designer should invest most of the effort that goes into a project by concentrating on the form, color, texture, and functionality of the materials that are used to create a space, rather than more formal, specific elements of style.

SYSTEMS FURNITURE

The tasks that were once common in most commercial businesses have changed or evolved, and the office environment has had to respond to these changes as well. The telephone—which is now used by everyone who spends time in an office—and the computer have become universal, and almost indispensable. Both of these tools require special electrical and communications wiring that enable them to operate in tandem with other machines.

Traditional furniture does a poor job at best of handling this equipment. For instance, when a computer is used on a traditional-style desk, there is little space left for writing and a bundle of wires inevitably hangs over the back of the desk. This may not be a problem for one or two workers, but it is almost overwhelming for larger offices, especially those with 100 employees or more.

In the early 1960s, a few furniture manufacturers began to study these kinds of problems, with the goal of creating a work environment that would be efficient, comfortable, and flexible enough to solve problems as a company grew or otherwise changed. The result of these studies was systems furniture.

Basically, systems furniture consists of a grouping of components that, when assembled in a specific way, result in an efficient workspace. The components can be put together with relative ease in a variety of configurations, depending on the needs of the user. It is the number of variations possible and the efficient utilization of space that makes systems furniture so successful.

COMPONENTS AND MODULARITY

Systems furniture is made up of five basic components: the panel, the worksurface, undercounter storage, overhead storage, and accessories. Each component is modular with others, making it possible to use them in a variety of configurations. It is assumed that the needs of almost any client can be met by simply finding the correct combination of components.

PANELS

The basic component of most systems furniture is the panel. Available in a range of widths and heights, panels are attached to one another end to end or in three- or four-way connections. A series of connected panels forms a sort of a skeleton to which the other components are attached, creating the potential for many workspace configurations. There are three panel characteristics that should be of concern to the interior designer: its construction, its method of connection to other panels, and its *wireways* or wiring system.

Because most of the system's components attach directly to the panel, exerting flexural and torsional forces on it, the panel should be as stable as possible. This must be accomplished while simultaneously making the panel as light as possible. As a result, a variety of techniques are used to create maximum stability while minimizing weight.

Many good-quality panels are constructed with a metal frame that is stabilized by reinforcing the connections at the corners; others use a solid plywood core. The construction is further strengthened by the insertion of a steel diaphragm. The edges of the panel are covered with a metal or plastic trim, and fabric is attached to the panel surfaces. The vertical metal edges on the sides of each panel, which are used to attach other components, are usually equipped with a series of slots spaced about 1 inch apart.

The panel edge may also contain a vertical channel to provide a path for cords and wires to run within the body of the panel, well out of sight. The top cap may be fitted with a horizontal channel for the same purpose. The bottom edge of the panel is the most important. It forms a base that supports the frame with adjustable feet and contains a special wire harness to conduct and distribute electrical power and space to run wiring for the telephone and computer. These elements give the system tremendous capabilities.

The method that each manufacturer uses to join one panel to another has a direct bearing on the system's strength and stability. This connection, whether straight or angular, is similar to the links of a chain. Just as a chain is only as strong as its weakest link, the stability and strength of a line of panels is a direct result of the stability and strength of their connections.

A typical panel is about 60 to 66 inches high. Most system panels are manufactured in 12-inch modules, which means that worksurfaces, shelving, and all other accessories are manufactured in 12-inch increments; commonly, lengths of 24, 36, 48, and 60 inches. In the interest of modularity, some manufacturers join their panels with a post-type connection, in which each panel is joined to the next by means of a vertical post whose horizontal extensions at top and bottom fit into corresponding extensions on the edge of each connecting panel. Because the panel is supported by these brackets, additional thickness for additional stability is less of a concern. The popularity of this type of panel connection has waned recently, mainly because every connection requires a post and connector regardless of whether it is joined to something else.

THE BASIC SYSTEMS FURNITURE PANEL CONSISTS OF A METAL FRAME TO WHICH FABRIC PANELS ARE ATTACHED. *COURTESY OF HERMAN MILLER, INC.*

(FAR LEFT) THE BASE AND BODY OF THE SYSTEMS PANEL CONTAIN WIREWAY CHANNELS THAT CAN EASILY ACCOMMODATE THE ELECTRICAL, TELEPHONE, AND COMPUTER WIRING NEEDS OF THE MODERN OFFICE. *(LEFT)* THE METHOD OF CONNECTION USED FOR SYSTEMS PANELS HAS A DIRECT BEARING ON THE FINISHED SYSTEM'S STABILITY *(BELOW)*. *COURTESY OF HERMAN MILLER, INC.*

A connection similar to the butt joint is another, more popular method used to attach system panels. For end-to-end connections, the panels are joined by means of either a continuous connector hinge or special brackets at top and bottom. These connections are quite simple and, other than the connector hinge or brackets, do not require any additional hardware. The main disadvantage of this type of connection occurs at angled joints, where the width of the adjoining panel (usually about 2 inches) must be added to the overall length of the entire group of panels. For example, when working with a row of four 6-foot-wide workstations, a designer must add 2 inches each time a panel is attached to the spine at a 90-degree angle. Therefore, four stations × 6 feet = 24 feet, plus five 90-degree panels × 2 inches = 10 inches. The sum is 24 feet, 10 inches. The designer must then ensure that the additional 10 inches can be accommodated; many designers are quite surprised to see that, once the furniture has been installed, there is simply not enough room for it because they neglected to take the additional length into account. The designer must then rework the layout in the hope of making it fit. If it does not, then he or she is forced to inform the client that their project will have one or two workstations less. Obviously, it is much simpler (and far less stressful) to make certain that the workstations fit before even ordering them.

With the increasing popularity of systems furniture in the workplace, the choices of panel fabrics have also increased. Manufacturers carefully investigate the durability of their fabric offerings, so that designers can be assured that they are suitable for most commercial projects. If a situation calls for a special or custom fabric, the designer should look into its specifications during the planning phase to confirm that its level of wearability will be appropriate, and have it approved by the panel manufacturer before ordering.

Because the surface of the panel on which the fabric is mounted is oriented vertically, and because the fabric is held in place only at the panel's edges, the fabric must be able to resist the tendency to sag under its own weight. As a result, most panel fabrics are densely woven and thin, which allows them to be stretched tightly across the panel while retaining their body and flat surface.

WORKSURFACES

Once the panels have been set up, the worksurface is the next component to be installed. Depending on the manufacturer, most systems worksurfaces are made from particleboard or steel and covered with plastic laminate. The front edge may be fitted with a rubber T-molding, a radiused edge, or other special shape, each of which is considered a "step up" from the plastic laminate and designed for economy, design, and ergonomics. The worksurface is attached to the panel by means of brackets fitted with angular teeth on either end that are inserted into the panel's slots, which are usually spaced in 1-inch increments.

Worksurfaces are available in a variety of sizes and configurations. The most common is the straight worksurface, which is manufactured in lengths that correspond to the available widths of the panels; depths are most commonly 18, 24, and 30 inches. The range of dimensions provides designers and clients with many choices.

In addition to the straight worksurface, there are several special configurations. One of the most popular is the corner unit. This is essentially a variation on the straight version, and is basically squared off at one end and angled or rounded on the other. This worksurface configuration enables the employee to make use of the corner space for something other than storage and is most commonly used for computers, as they tend to be wider than other office equipment. Another type of worksurface has a slot in the center, which allows computer paper to be stored below and fed through the slot to the printer.

UNDERCOUNTER STORAGE

Undercounter storage in system furniture is essentially the same as that in a standard desk, consisting of drawers that are commonly available in small, medium, and large sizes. The small drawers, which are also referred to as *pencil drawers*, are intended to store such items as pencils, pens, paper clips, pushpins, and rulers. Many times they are fitted with a small tray that divides its interior space. The middle-sized drawers are known as *boxes*. Most manufacturers make an accessory unit for the box drawer that is fitted with six to eight slanted shelves for storing stationery and envelopes. The large drawers, or *file drawers*, are designed to store files, but can also store bulky items that are used infrequently or need to be hidden from sight.

All the drawers are stacked one on the top of another to form a pedestal that can be either attached to the worksurface or mounted on casters for mobility. The designer can arrange them in several configurations; two examples, from top to bottom, might be box, box, and file, or pencil, box, and file. To provide convenient, flexible storage for the life of the system, some manufacturers make each drawer a separate unit that the client can restack as needed.

OVERHEAD STORAGE

Overhead storage, or an upper storage unit, is available in two forms: open shelving and enclosed shelving. Its main function is to keep information at the employee's fingertips while leaving worksurface space open. As the term implies, *open shelving* is simply traditional shelving that is used to store books, binders, papers, and other supplies.

AN ASSEMBLED
SYSTEMS
WORKSTATION,
COMPLETE
WITH A ROLL-IN
KEYBOARD DRAWER,
OVERHEAD
ENCLOSED SHELVING
AND UNDERCOUNTER
STORAGE, AND
METAL AND PLASTIC
ORGANIZERS.
*COURTESY OF
HERMAN MILLER, INC.*

Enclosed shelving, which is also commonly referred to as *binder bins* or *flipper door units*, are simply shelves that have sides, a top, and a door that hides their contents. Some styles of enclosed shelving flip the door over the top of the unit to open it, which prevents the employee from placing anything on top of it. This may be desirable if a clean, unobstructed look is the goal. In other styles, the door is slid under the top of the unit, which leaves the space there open for plants and other decorative items. For an additional degree of flexibility, some units are manufactured so that the top and door can be removed. Enclosed shelving can also be fitted with locks to provide secure storage.

ACCESSORIES

The category of accessories includes those items, large and small, that serve to finish the system and make work-related tasks easier and more convenient. One of the basic goals of systems furniture is to keep the the worksurface as uncluttered as possible in order to leave room for tasks. Consequently, any accessory that helps in this regard is important. By using a variety of methods, these accessories may be attached to the panel, just as the other components are. Although it would be impossible here to enumerate all of the accessories available, designers should at least familiarize themselves with manufacturers' literature so that they are aware of their options.

One of the most common component accessories is the basket or organizer in which papers and active files are stored. These baskets are actually metal or plastic dividers that are placed within shelves or directly on the panels by means of brackets. They can be oriented horizontally, vertically, or at an angle, and can be changed to fulfill new tasks as they arise.

Another common accessory is a small shelf on a movable arm on which a phone or calculator can be kept handy but still out of the way. Still another is an adjustable computer keyboard holder. In some cases, this is simply a drawer that is attached to the bottom of the worksurface, which allows the keyboard to be pushed out of the way when it is not being used. Other keyboard holders are attached to a movable arm, enabling the user to adjust the keyboard in an almost infinite number of positions.

The larger accessories are simply those pieces of furniture that are intended to be incorporated into the system as they are needed. These include file cabinets, storage cabinets, and wardrobes, some of which are made in traditional styles, while others are available in colors or textures that blend with the rest of the system. Some of these pieces can be attached directly to the panel to accomplish the same task more efficiently.

WIRING CONSIDERATIONS

Because conventional offices are limited in their ability to accommodate the extent of wiring that is now common in the office environment, systems furniture's capacity to handle electrical and communications requirements with relative ease is one of its most important functional features. Traditionally, all electrical, phone, and computer wiring is plugged into wall or floor outlets that one could only hope are conveniently located. Unfortunately, in many instances they are not, especially in open-office layouts where access to structural walls is at a minimum and the majority of desks are equipped with computers, phones, and other electric-powered devices. In such an arrangement, any change in the location of an electrical outlet or in phone and data communications requires an electrician or other installation specialist.

Understandably, in an attempt to avoid inconvenience and expense, clients often try to solve such matters themselves. However, in addition to looking unfinished and extremely unattractive, extension cords that are taped to the floor across aisles or walkways are illegal.

As mentioned above, the base of the systems panel is reserved for electrical and communication wireways. However, a furniture system provides more than a channel through which standard electrical wiring can be run. Manufacturers also offer *modular wiring systems*, which have been approved by Underwriters Laboratories as safe and meeting all code requirements. This type of wiring system makes it possible to easily connect the wiring between each panel during assembly by the furniture installers. An electrician is needed only to hook the end of the panels' electrical circuit to the building by means of a specially designed *pig tail*, or power-in connector. Each manufacturer's set of wireways differs slightly from the others, but they all snap together and use connectors where the outlets are fastened, which makes them simple to install and change later.

Phone and communications lines have a different set of considerations. While most phone systems use either a solid or stranded wire, many computer systems use *coax*, or *coaxial cable*, which is a single strand of wire covered with heavy insulation and a foil or braided wire shield to keep out outside interference. As might be expected, technology is always evolving. A number of computer networks transmit data via *twisted-pair wires*, and the latest technology uses *fiber optics*. Regardless of the means used to transmit information, all office phones and computer equipment need to be physically connected to a shared network. Systems furniture very conveniently allots space in the base of each panel for up to nine phone cables about 1/4 inch each in diameter. This is usually adequate, but if more space is needed, most manufacturers can accommodate additional cables in a channel at the top of each panel or with an *add-on raceway*. These raceways are connected to the base cavity by channels that run vertically along both edges of the panels, allowing wires to be run in almost any configuration.

QUALITY

Quality is somewhat difficult to discern in systems furniture. Most manufacturers work very hard on their product's appearance in order to make them suitable for a professional environment. However, looks are quickly forgotten when a system does not function well under normal and expected wear. In addition, the system that works well for one client may not be at all appropriate for another. Therefore, designers should educate themselves and their clients about the assets and liabilities of each company's product. There are three major areas that a designer should consider when evaluating the quality of a system: its durability, flexibility, and simplicity.

Durability is probably the foremost reason to choose a particular brand of systems furniture. There are a few ways to determine whether a system is reasonably durable. The first concerns movement: If a system installation is adequately strong—which is directly affected by how the panels and components are attached to one another—a row of panels should not move appreciably when pushed on, and a worksurface should be strong enough for someone to sit on. Drawers and flipper doors should open and close smoothly without twisting or racking. If movement is found to be excessive in any of these tests, it may suggest future problems. This does not mean that the system must be entirely indestructible, but those who use the system should be able to perform their jobs without worrying about damaging it.

MATERIALS

For a variety of reasons, the majority of custom furniture is made of wood. During the custom process, the beauty of wood is significantly enhanced with the use of special joinery, veneers, and finishing techniques. Also, the public perceives that wood furniture communicates success, and custom wood furniture is simply an additional step toward status. Still another reason for the popularity of wood is its relative economy. Although custom furniture is more expensive than standard furniture, its cost is reduced somewhat when it is produced in wood rather than in stone, metal, or other materials that require highly specialized skills and machinery.

While its use lags significantly behind that of wood, stone—including marble and granite—is the next most popular material used in custom furniture. Stone is used primarily as the top surface of such pieces as desks, tables, and credenzas. The major limitation of stone is its weight; unfortunately, it may become brittle when cut thin to a very veneer. As a result, stone must be carefully specified within appropriate dimensions. This is usually not a problem, as long as the designer consults with both the stone supplier and furniture manufacturer to ensure that his or her design is workable.

Metal is also occasionally used to build custom furniture. Invitations to build custom metal furniture are usually extended to manufacturers that have the proper tools and extensive experience. However, because this type of work is costly and disruptive, many manufacturers will not even consider it. Currently, the designs of most custom metal furniture are limited to heavily scaled pieces that can be built from common steel, cut and bent in a fabrication shop, welded or bolted together, and painted or plated.

ADVANTAGES AND DISADVANTAGES

The advantages of custom-built furniture are obvious: Both the client and the designer get the look, functionality, and configuration that was desired. Occasionally, if a piece performs properly, more will be built to match. Many pieces of furniture that are now standard originated as custom pieces.

There are, however, several disadvantages to custom furniture. As discussed earlier, clients will get exactly what they want, but they must be willing to pay more for it. Researching and obtaining special species of wood and veneers, milling special shapes or sizes, unique staining and finishing processes, and painstaking assembly by expert artisans are all more labor-intensive, and therefore more expensive. Within the limits of the budget, the client must decide whether a custom piece is worth the price.

Another disadvantage of custom furniture concerns a piece's of relationship to the space for which it is built and its specific intended purpose. When a piece of custom furniture is built into a site, it is consequently very difficult to move. This means that the client is usually forced to leave it where it was installed, even if the company moves. If the piece can somehow be moved, the original location is drastically altered; in the new location, the piece will most likely not retain the quality of "fit" it had in its original location. In addition, because a piece of custom furniture is usually built for a specific task, when the task changes it does not adapt easily. The example that follows serves to illustrate this point.

During renovation, the client representing a small bank requested that the designer propose plans for a "deal table," where a group of employees could trade investments and stocks. The designer had a table custom-built that could accommodate six employees. The two lazy Susans in the center of the table each held a stock monitor, which was to be shared by three people. In addition, each lazy Susan had a recessed keyboard slot. While they did not expect to use the phone continuously while working at the table, the employees needed access to telephones, so the designer had phone drawers added. This arrangement was satisfactory until advancements in computer technology produced monitors small enough that six could be accommodated on the table, and the phones were adapted for headsets. These developments made the lazy Susans, their recessed keyboards, and the phone drawers completely obsolete. As a result, the table was adapted to the new situation, but it never functioned as well as it had initially.

Rather than discouraging designers from considering custom furniture as an option, the case above shows that they must make sure that their clients fully understand both the costs and limitations of what can be a beautiful and satisfying alternative to standard furniture.

QUALITY

The evaluation of a piece of custom furniture's quality usually considers the character of both its materials and workmanship. As was mentioned earlier, because custom furniture is made exactly to a designer's specifications, the level of quality should be in accordance with the designer's wishes. When the function of the piece is of primary importance, the yardsticks of quality—and probably price—become secondary. When a piece's appearance is the main concern—which is also when custom furniture really shines and a designer can best exhibit his or her talent—materials and workmanship will undoubtedly play leading roles in its evaluation. Within the constraints of budget and style set by the client, the space, the designer's ability, and the limitations of the materials, the sky is the limit.

The most popular locations for custom furniture are such high-visibility sites as reception areas and conference rooms. Often, the consideration of status alone justifies additional cost, and the advantage gained by unique pieces of furniture may dictate that they are necessary.

ORDERING PROCEDURES

A designer cannot order a piece of custom furniture simply because he or she has envisioned it. To "sell" the idea to the client, the designer presents a sketch of the piece. The next step depends on who will build the piece. If the designer has a good relationship with an artisan, a meeting to discuss what is required for the particular piece may be all that is necessary. Before beginning construction, the artisan creates working drawings, which must then be approved by both the client and the designer.

If the designer doesn't have an established relationship with an artisan, or if the project will be bid on competitively, it is strongly recommended that the designer familiarize him- or herself with the general procedures and standards of the proposed materials and prepare drawings of the piece. These may be full working drawings that the artisan would use to build the piece; at the very least, they should be conceptual drawings that show top and side views, and indicate configuration, size, materials, hardware, finishes, and other details. In either case, the artisan or bidders should have a reasonably good idea of what is needed.

13

CASEWORK

AND

CUSTOM TRIM

USED ELEGANTLY, CASEWORK AND CUSTOM TRIM CAN ENHANCE A WIDE RANGE OF SPACES, INCLUDING RECEPTION AREAS, EXECUTIVE OFFICES, AND LIBRARIES. *PHOTO BY LINCOLN ALLEN*

As it is used in this book, the term *casework* refers to any cabinetry, shelving, or other furnishings that are built into or otherwise attached to the interior substructures of a building. *Custom trim* is milled or shaped pieces of wood or wood products that are specifically designed and created to frame the perimeters of windows, doors, and casework. Continuous trim configurations such as crown moldings, baseboards, and wainscoting are used to conceal or ornament joints. Plastic and resin-based trims are also used with premanufactured casework, as a transition element between adjacent walls, floors, or columns.

In early office settings, freestanding furniture was virtually the only type of furnishing that a worker used to perform his or her job. Except for banks, law offices, and other executive facilities where such expense could be justified, casework in any configuration was rarely used. As technological advancements evolved and the economy expanded, corporate environments were conceived to acknowledge the needs and comfort of workers, and various furniture and casework systems were incorporated to meet those needs. Today, depending on the materials used and the complexity of the work, built-in casework in the forms of kitchen cabinetry in workrooms and breakrooms, shelving in storage rooms and libraries, and special configurations built in conjunction with freestanding furniture are all reasonably affordable.

CASEWORK

Because every site and client's needs are different, casework must be specially built for each location or function. The other defining characteristic of casework is that some of the work must be done on the installation site.

There are two basic categories of casework: custom and modular or premanufactured. *Custom casework* is made to precise specifications to fit a specific location. The designer consults with his or her client to determine what is desired or needed, measures the site, then sketches or draws up a workable design. After a price and craftsperson or custom manufacturer are agreed upon, more measurements are taken to ensure that the designed piece or pieces can actually be built as drawn. The casework is then manufactured piece by piece. In many cases, it will be partially assembled and transported to the site, where final cutting and fitting will take place. When completed, the casework will be immediately adjacent or affixed to the building's substructures.

Although in most instances the members of each discipline conduct themselves in a professionally generous and respectful manner, it should be noted that the potential for conflict within the interior designer/craftsperson relationship exists. It is clear that each is an expert in his or her respective field, and that by necessity each must complement the other, but there is a point at which individual experience and opinion concerning aesthetics, planning, manufacturing, and execution can—and on occasion do—become the source of friction. When contracting for their services, clients essentially ask interior designers to use their creativity and experience to help solve the problem of realizing a vision of their interior space. In the course of the problem's solution, designers must consult with other professionals and experts where their knowledge or experience is lacking. Craftspeople or manufacturers of custom products contribute their intimate understanding of the limitations and capabilities of the material, wood, as well as its related construction and installation techniques. Unless a designer has spent time working in a woodworking shop, he or she will probably not have the same level of knowledge of custom casework construction and installation, particularly when a unique situation arises. At the risk of belaboring a point, if each party has respect for the other's abilities, then the client—and the project—will most likely benefit from those of both.

The term *premanufactured casework,* which implies that the finished piece is similar to freestanding furniture in that it is made in the factory and delivered to the site, is actually a bit of a misnomer. Premanufactured casework is made to somewhat flexible configurations, which allow for installation in a wide variety of situations with minimal on-site work that still accommodates a "built-in" look.

The modularity of premanufactured casework is a result of a range of predetermined sizes. Cabinetry similar to that used in residential kitchens is the most popular type of premanufactured casework. The basic configurations consist of base cabinets, wall cabinets, sink cabinets, and full-height storage cabinets, all of which are available in a few standard heights. For instance, wall cabinets are most commonly manufactured in heights of 12, 15, 18, 24, and 30 inches, with corresponding widths usually available in 3-inch increments. Filler strips are used to fill remaining space when the site does not conform to a standard width. In addition, manufacturers usually offer a reasonable variety of casework styles and wood types and finishes.

The standard configurations and sizes will accommodate most sites and conditions. The majority of manufacturers can fabricate special configurations for a moderate increase in price and time allowance, although the degree of flexibility and product variety vary among manufacturers and depends in part on the demands of the local market. The range in style and sensibility of the craftspeople who service a specific geographical area will enable most designers to find at least one whose work fits their needs.

STANDARDS

In order to inform interior designers and their clients about what to expect from casework and trim manufacturers, designers, and installers, the American Woodwork Institute publishes an extensive manual of standards and grade categories that govern all aspects of architectural woodwork.

Three grades have been established to encompass most of the quality and cost constraints for the casework in any project— premium, custom, and economy—whose standards generally reflect those of the wood industry. While it is acknowledged that there are many ways to perform a particular task, these standards specify what is deemed best from a consensus of those who represent the industry. Because it is not within the scope of this book to fully define the restrictions of each grade for every situation, it is strongly recommended that interior designers familiarize themselves with the handbook's specifications. Just as they expect custom casework manufacturers to carefully examine and implement their specifications and drawings, interior designers should at least possess a general awareness and understanding of the requirements of this field.

The *premium grade* specifies the highest standards of both workmanship and materials, with an emphasis on aesthetics and integrity of construction. For casework of this grade, the quality of lumber and veneer is highly controlled. The joints of main body members must be mitered and glued, and attached trim must be of a specified thinness and also glued. Shelves or other members must have dado joints to hide edges. Gaps between doors and joint tolerances are limited to absolute minimums. Unless the design specifies otherwise, face veneers must be matched across doors and drawers. Casework that satisfies these standards is usually the most expensive.

While the quality of its products is not as high as those judged as premium grade, the standards for *custom grade* casework are still high for materials and construction. Compared with those outlined for premium grade, custom grade restrictions on the quality of materials are less restrictive. This standard specifies that while some joints need not be mitered, they must be glued and nailed. Attached trim can be of any thickness but must be also be glued and nailed. Dado joints may be used if the finish is opaque or if a laminate is used. Gap and joint tolerances are not as restrictive as those allowed for premium grade, but are still limiting. Face veneers need not be matched across doors and drawers, but the grain of a particular section must be oriented in the long direction. The result is good-quality casework whose aesthetics are at least reasonable.

Economy grade casework is usually specified when cost is the primary consideration. The requirements regarding the quality of materials and veneers are the least restrictive of the three grades but ensure that the final product will have reasonable strength and integrity. The economy grade standards stipulate that most joints must be nailed but not necessarily glued. Trim may be of any thickness and need only be nailed. Gaps and spaces between doors and drawers are even less restrictive than those required for a custom grade. Dado joints need not have hidden edges, and face veneers need not be oriented in any specific direction. In spite of what seems to be a lack of requirements, the economy grade does not give manufacturers free reign to build casework in whatever manner they deem appropriate. This category outlines minimum standards of quality to ensure that, with reasonable care and maintenance, the product will provide good service for the cost.

The allure of casework is that it can be built to accomplish a variety of tasks, and can meet a wide range of special design requirements while retaining a high degree of economy. If they are familiar with the advantages as well as the limitations of this area of interior design, designers can enhance their practices immeasurably.

CUSTOM TRIM

To say that a trim or molding is "custom" simply means that it has been made to a special shape. Standard trims and moldings are made by running a length of wood through a shaper that is fitted with a multi-edged bit or head. The cutting surfaces of the bit are shaped so that the wood is molded to the desired shape. Custom trim is also milled in much the same way, although the methods used are somewhat different.

In one technique, a length of wood is run through the shaper several times, and each time the bit or head is changed or the wood is run through in a different position to create unique shapes. The designer should be aware of the standard shapes that are available so that he or she can request pleasing combinations.

The other method involves the use of special cutting heads, which gives the designer tremendous latitude in choosing and creating trims for a project. If a configuration cannot be achieved by combining standard shapes or by varying the position through which the wood is run through the shaper, the designer may arrange for a special cutting head to be cast. If the order is substantial, the manufacturer may agree to absorb at least part of the additional cost for this type of work. (For a discussion of standard wood trim and molding, see Chapter 2, "Wood.")

A SELECTION OF WOOD TRIMS AND MOLDINGS. *COURTESY OF WOOD MOULDING & MILLWORK PRODUCERS ASSOCIATION, PORTLAND, OREGON*

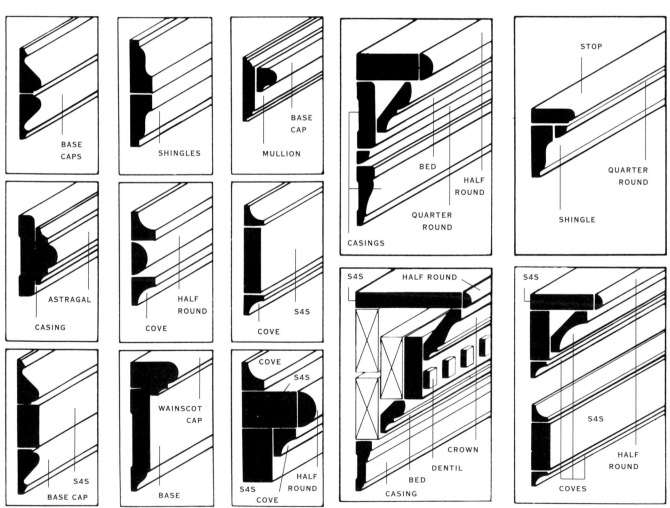

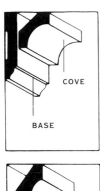

COVE

BASE

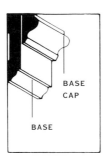

BASE
CAP

BASE

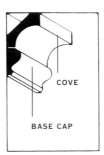

COVE

BASE CAP

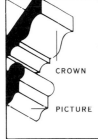

CROWN

PICTURE

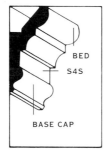

BED
S4S

BASE CAP

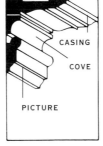

CASING
COVE

PICTURE

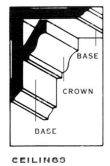

BASE

CROWN

BASE

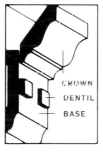

CROWN
DENTIL
BASE

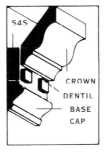

S4S

CROWN
DENTIL
BASE
CAP

CEILINGS

BACK
BAND

CASING

CASING

BASE
CAP

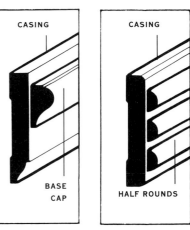

CASING

HALF ROUNDS

PANEL

CASING

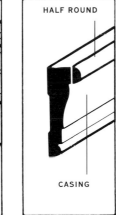

HALF ROUND

CASING

COVE

QUARTER
ROUND

CASING

DOORS AND WINDOWS

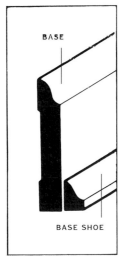

BASE

BASE SHOE

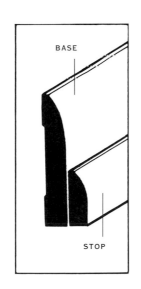

BASE

STOP

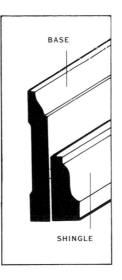

BASE

SHINGLE

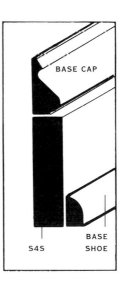

BASE CAP

S4S

BASE
SHOE

BED

S4S

BASE
SHOE

BASES

219

14

FINISH EVALUATION, SPECIFICATION, AND SCHEDULING

THE FINISHES IN THIS ELEGANT INTERIOR HAVE BEEN SELECTED NOT ONLY FOR THEIR BEAUTY BUT ALSO FOR THEIR SUITABILITY. *PHOTOGRAPHY BY JON MILLER, HEDRICH-BLESSING; POWELL/KLEINSCHMIDT, INTERIOR ARCHITECTS*

As can be easily deduced from the focus of this book—the finishes that are used in contract interiors, their specific characteristics, how they are fabricated or manufactured, and how they are installed— a significant part of the practice of contract interior design involves working with interior finish materials. The basic process requires a proper evaluation of prospective materials, a choice of finish, and specifications that outline for the client, the bidder, and the contractor which finishes have been chosen and where and by what general procedures they will be installed.

Understanding and engaging in this process gives the designer the tools by which he or she will make an appropriate decision. This chapter looks at which characteristics a designer should evaluate to decide which finishes are suitable for a particular project, how to communicate those decisions to all parties involved, and how to ensure that finishes are placed and installed properly.

EVALUATION

Since choosing finishes is an essential part of any interior design project, it is assumed that the designer will exert significant effort in determining whether or not a particular finish is appropriate for an intended area or use. A responsible finish evaluation, regardless of the number of elements, must consider much more than a finish's superficial physical characteristics. As should be apparent from the preceding chapters, there are a number of other properties that are equally important. Because a designer is working on behalf of his or her client, it stands to reason that any finish should be examined in view of the client's needs and concerns.

VISUAL AND TEXTURAL CONCERNS

In spite of the fact that a designer must at some later point in the process assess its other characteristics, a finish's color, shading, texture, and shape are most probably the among first that are considered when it is evaluated. These aspects are all important, as they are related to the aesthetic element of a project. In addition, many designers take considerable pride in their talent for choosing and mixing a variety of finishes.

Because manufacturers' materials and processes vary, it would be virtually impossible—not to mention undesirable—to standardize colors and textures for all finish manufacturers. In addition, the quality of light in a space and any adjacent or accompanying finishes affect the look and presentation of a finish as well. For these reasons, a designer first prepares samples of each finish and evaluates them together under a similar intensity of light to determine to how well they blend or go together, then uses the samples to assemble a *color board*, which enables the client to examine and approve the designer's finish ideas. Any concerns relating to color, texture, and so forth should be addressed before the other aspects of the finish are taken into consideration.

QUALITY

Regardless of how well a finish looks, if it does not perform well it is not a good choice. The designer should consult the product data published by the manufacturer for guidelines regarding intended use. In most cases, each finish material has established industry standards that categorize products with similar physical and characteristics to help the designer properly evaluate the finishes, thereby avoiding potential problems.

For instance, commercial carpeting has a "heavy traffic" standard, which means that a product so marked is manufactured to specifications that enable it to perform satisfactorily in such environments as airports or restaurants. Wallcoverings with a Type I classification indicate that products complying with that category's requirements are suitable for installation in areas of moderate use, not heavy or intense use.

AVAILABILITY AND DELIVERY

Many projects have been ruined or delayed because a particular product was either not available when it was needed or delivered late. The designer should always confirm availability and delivery schedules with the supplier or installer before committing to a product.

Most designers who have worked in the field for more than a few years have experienced availability problems. Consider, for instance, the designer who based her entire project on a particular patterned carpet.

The other finishes were coordinated with the carpet's background and pattern colors, its price fit the budget, and the client was pleased with and approved the choice. The required drawings and documents were completed and the designer put the project out for bid. The designer then received a call from one of the carpet bidders. The bidder had called the carpet manufacturer and found that because the carpet was so popular there was a two-month back order on it; she wanted to know if another carpet could be substituted. When the designer investigated the problem, she found that because the carpet's pattern and colors were unique a substitute could not be used without recoordinating the finishes for the entire project.

Unfortunately, the first (and best) remedy to this problem, a suitable alternative to the first choice of carpet, was unacceptable, since it involved rechoosing all the other finishes. Waiting until the carpet could be delivered was also unacceptable because the client had already scheduled to open for business by a certain date. It was discovered that a carpet could be special-ordered from another manufacturer to match the original color and pattern, and though it could be delivered on time its cost was somewhat higher. While this situation would normally also be unacceptable, under the circumstances it was the most practical.

Having to choose a last-minute alternative may also mean a sacrifice in the quality of the design. Because the average client may not be as conscious of a product's or finish's quality as an interior designer, the alternative that the designer considers substandard may be satisfactory to the client. In some instances, even the situation described above is not possible and additional time and costs are necessary. In any event, the designer's competence in the eyes of his or her client may be diminished, but this is sometimes inevitable. If a designer consistently checks to ensure the availability of all products specified for a project, then all but unforseeable problems will be greatly reduced.

PRODUCT PERFORMANCE AND TRACK RECORD

The majority of finishes are designed to perform in a predictable manner when they are properly installed. Regrettably, how a product is supposed to perform and how it actually functions on the job can be quite different. Because most manufacturers cannot take ten (or even three to five) years to study their products' performance, short-term, high-intensity tests that subject the product to conditions that are far more severe than actual conditions are devised to determine performance data. The theory is that these kinds of tests will indicate an equivalent level of wear over several years, though they obviously do not always provide an accurate picture of a product's performance. There is simply no substitute for on-the-job product testing: Wearability, lightfastness, and other characteristics are best tested over an extended period of time.

For example, when the synthetic fiber olefin was first used to manufacture carpeting, it was touted as a "state-of-the-art" synthetic material: Manufacturers' tests indicated that it would wear and look well, the quality of color was similar to that of wool, and there was no static generation. After a few years of actual on-the-job wear, however, it was found to have a tendency to mat down, especially in heavy traffic situations. Although the pile could be lifted with a good vacuuming, it would mat down again almost immediately. As a result, many installations had to be replaced after just a few years. The manufacturers alleviated this problem to some extent by using a higher, denser face weight to help the fibers resist crushing, but olefin fiber is still not recommended for use in heavy traffic areas.

When investigating a new product, it is recommended that the designer either ask to see reports on actual installations or visit an installation if possible. When a designer recommends a product, the client expects that he or she is familiar with and can vouch for its performance. If a product has any limitations, the designer should discuss them with the client so that he or she will be comfortable with the chosen finish.

PRICE

Of course, every designer would prefer to choose a project's finishes and products without having to consider cost. This is simply not possible for the majority of clients. In fact, cost is often the driving force behind a designer's finish choices. When working within very tight budgets, the choices can be quite limited.

Depending on how a designer approaches a project, the limits imposed by a budget can create either a handicap or a challenge. In either case, the designer will need to expend a bit more energy in finding suitable materials that fit the budget and work within the design. With a little ingenuity, the results can be at least pleasing, and can sometimes be surprisingly striking.

Regardless of budgetary constraints, a designer should be aware of the general price range of any product or finish that he or she chooses to specify for a project; to not do so would be a great disservice to a client. This does not mean, however, that a material whose price is somewhat higher than what was budgeted for should not be considered at all. On the contrary, if a product is a perfect "fit," the designer should discuss it with the client. If the client cannot accommodate the additional cost, then obviously another choice must be made. Though for many projects (and clients) the budget is somewhat flexible, the designer should ensure that, as the selection of finishes and products are finalized, the finished project will fit the program financially as well as conceptually.

SPECIFICATION

The specification of materials is as crucial to a successful interior design program as the designer's evaluation. In writing the specifications, the designer outlines exactly which finishes he or she has chosen. Although this may seem to be a fairly simple task, it can also be the source of many headaches. A brief example serves best to illustrate the potential problems.

A designer selected tile for the rest rooms of a commercial office building. His design required different colors for the men's and women's rest rooms. A color board had been submitted to the client and approved. After construction on the project had begun, the tile installer submitted sample boards so that final color choices could be made. This surprised the designer, as he was certain that he had already chosen the colors. The installer claimed to be following the specifications, which indicated that colors were to be chosen from the Group A price category. These tiles were the least expensive, with colors limited to whites and off-whites. The designer then had two choices: to choose from among the installer's offerings, or to ask the client to approve a change order for what had been approved originally, which meant additional expense.

When writing the final specifications for these materials, the designer had used the standard wall and floor tile format of the Masterspec® Specifications System (a product of the Professional Systems Division of the American Institute of Architects. The standard format for resilient tile flooring appears on pages 228 to 234 as an example.) As this format covers all aspects of the material and indicates at the end of each section how it should be edited, it is clear that the designer simply did not read and edit the written specifications thoroughly.

While it is essential that designers know what is in their specifications, it is not necessary for specifications to be lengthy and complicated. On a small project, the designer may choose to name the manufacturer, pattern, and color of each finish, which would leave no doubt as to what has been chosen. For larger projects, however, the specifications cannot be exact: The designer must specify finishes generically—based on performance rather than noted by brand name—so that several contractors can propose competitive bids based on estimates from more than one manufacturer. Public projects are required by law in many states to have at least three different manufacturers from whom the finishes can be purchased.

While it is not within the scope of this book to discuss the specification of interior finishes in depth, the designer should be aware of a few guidelines. First, the specifications should be tailored to fit the job and its management. Normally, if a project requires bids, a more involved set of specifications will be needed to properly specify the product or products. The contractors' price estimates will be more competitive if more than one item can be specified. This is relatively easy to do for such finishes as wood, paint, wallcovering, and laminates. For finishes such as carpeting and furniture, however, it is much more difficult to invite competitive bidding without possibly compromising the item's color, design, or quality. Second, the designer must be prepared to take responsibility for the content of the specifications, especially when contractors will be invited to bid on a project. Also, the designer should confirm that the manufacturer's specifications match the product described in the specification. It is acceptable to stipulate exactly which product and color is desired, then follow it immediately with the phrase "or designer-approved equal." This means that the product described is what is intended; if the bidding contractor can supply a similar item for an equal or lower price, the designer must first approve the substitute.

SECTION 09660 - RESILIENT TILE FLOORING

THIS SECTION USES THE TERM ARCHITECT. CHANGE THIS TERM AS NECESSARY TO MATCH ACTUAL TERM USED TO IDENTIFY DESIGN PROFESSIONAL AS DEFINED IN GENERAL AND SUPPLEMENTARY CONDITIONS.

PART 1 - GENERAL

RELATED DOCUMENTS

Drawings and general provisions of the Contract, including General and Supplementary Conditions and Division 1 Specification Sections, apply to this Section.

SUMMARY

This Section includes the following:

ADJUST LIST BELOW TO SUIT PROJECT.

Homogenous (solid) vinyl floor tile.

Rubber floor tile.

Vinyl composition floor tile.

LIST ONLY PRODUCTS, CONSTRUCTION, AND EQUIPMENT INCLUDED IN THIS PROJECT THAT THE READER WOULD EXPECT TO FIND IN THIS SECTION. VERIFY THAT SECTIONS LISTED ARE INCLUDED IN THIS SPECIFICATION AND THAT THEIR TITLES ARE CORRECT.

Resilient wall base, reducer strips, and other accessories installed with resilient floor tiles are specified in Division 9 Section "Resilient Wall Base and Accessories."

SUBMITTALS

General: Submit the following in accordance with Conditions of Contract and Division 1 Specification Sections.

Product data for each type of product specified.

DELETE BELOW IF NO REGULATIONS ON VOLATILE ORGANIC COMPOUNDS.

Certification by tile manufacturer that products supplied for tile installation comply with local regulations controlling use of volatile organic compounds (VOC's).

Samples for initial selection purposes in form of manufacturer's color charts consisting of actual tiles or sections of tiles showing full range of colors and patterns available for each type of resilient floor tile indicated.

Samples for verification purposes in full-size tiles of each different color and pattern of resilient floor tile specified, showing full range of variations expected in these characteristics.

┌───┐
│ DELETE BELOW IF NOT ALLOWED.   │
└───┘

Product certificates, in lieu of laboratory test reports when permitted by Architect, signed by manufacturer certifying that each product complies with requirements.

Maintenance data for resilient floor tile, to include in Operating and Maintenance Manual specified in Division 1.

QUALITY ASSURANCE

Single-Source Responsibility for Floor Tile: Obtain each type, color, and pattern of tile from a single source with resources to provide products of consistent quality in appearance and physical properties without delaying progress of the Work.

┌───┐
│ DELETE BELOW IF NOT REQUIRED BY AUTHORITIES HAVING JURISDICTION. SEE EDITING INSTRUCTION NO. 1 BEFORE │
│ RETAINING.   │
└───┘

Fire Performance Characteristics: Provide resilient floor tile with the following fire performance characteristics as determined by testing products per ASTM test method indicated below by UL or another testing and inspecting agency acceptable to authorities having jurisdiction.

Critical Radiant Flux: 0.45 watts per sq. cm or more per ASTM E 648.

Smoke Density: Less than 450 per ASTM E 662.

DELIVERY, STORAGE, AND HANDLING

Deliver tiles and installation accessories to Project site in original manufacturer's unopened cartons and containers each bearing names of product and manufacturer, Project identification, and shipping and handling instructions.

Store flooring materials in dry spaces protected from the weather with ambient temperatures maintained between 50 deg F (10 deg C) and 90 deg F (32 deg C).

Store tiles on flat surfaces. Move tiles and installation accessories into spaces where they will be installed at least 48 hours in advance of installation.

PROJECT CONDITIONS

Maintain a minimum temperature of 70 deg F (21 deg C) in spaces to receive tiles for at least 48 hours prior to installation, during installation, and for not less than 48 hours after installation. After this period, maintain a temperature of not less than 55 deg F (13 deg C).

Do not install tiles until they are at the same temperature as the space where they are to be installed.

Close spaces to traffic during tile installation.

SEQUENCING AND SCHEDULING

RESILIENT TILE FLOORING   09660 - 2

Subfloors are free of cracks, ridges, depressions, scale, and foreign deposits of any kind.

> DELETE PARAGRAPH AND SUBPARAGRAPHS UNDER IT IF NO WOOD FLOORS. CORRELATE WITH DIVISION 6 SECTION "ROUGH CARPENTRY" TO ENSURE THAT UNDERLAYMENT MATERIAL AND INSTALLATION METHOD SPECIFIED ARE ACCEPTABLE TO RESILIENT FLOORING MFR.

For wood subfloors verify the following:

> BELOW ASSUMES UNDERLAYMENT IS SPECIFIED AS PREFERRED BY RESILIENT FLOORING MFRS. IF RESILIENT FLOORING IS APPLIED DIRECTLY TO SUBFLOOR, REVISE BELOW AND VERIFY ACCEPTABILITY WITH RESILIENT FLOORING MFR.

Underlayment over subfloor complies with requirements specified in Division 6 "Rough Carpentry."

Underlayment surface is free of surface irregularities and substances with potential to interfere with adhesive bond, show through surface, or stain tile.

> IF TILES WILL BE APPLIED OVER OTHER FORMS OF SUBFLOORS INCLUDING OLD CONCRETE AND EXISTING RESILIENT FLOORING, INSERT EXAMINATION REQUIREMENTS HERE AND PREPARATION REQUIREMENTS IN ARTICLE BELOW.

Do not proceed with installation until unsatisfactory conditions have been corrected.

PREPARATION

> NOTE THAT MORE EXTENSIVE SURFACE PREPARATION IS REQUIRED OVER EXISTING FLOORING. ACTUAL REQUIREMENTS VARY WITH INDIVIDUAL MFRS. ADD SPECIAL INSTRUCTIONS TO SUIT PROJECT.

General: Comply with manufacturer's installation specifications to prepare substrates indicated to receive tile.

Use trowelable leveling and patching compounds per tile manufacturer's directions to fill cracks, holes, and depressions in substrates.

Remove coatings, including curing compounds, and other substances that are incompatible with flooring adhesives and that contain soap, wax, oil, or silicone, by using a terrazzo or concrete grinder, a drum sander, or a polishing machine equipped with a heavy-duty wire brush.

Broom or vacuum clean substrates to be covered by tiles immediately before tile installation. Following cleaning, examine substrates for moisture, alkaline salts, carbonation, or dust.

Apply concrete slab primer, if recommended by flooring manufacturer, prior to applying adhesive. Apply according to manufacturer's directions.

INSTALLATION

General: Comply with tile manufacturer's installation directions and other requirements indicated that are applicable to each type of tile installation included in Project.

> REVISE BELOW IF FLOOR GEOMETRY OR PATTERN DICTATES ANOTHER RELATIONSHIP OF TILES WITH ROOM AXIS.

RESILIENT TILE FLOORING   09660 - 5

Lay out tiles from center marks established with principal walls, discounting minor offsets, so tiles at opposite edges of room are of equal width. Adjust as necessary to avoid using cut widths at perimeter that equal less than one-half of a tile. Install tiles square with room axis, unless otherwise indicated.

Match tiles for color and pattern by selecting tiles from cartons in same sequence as manufactured and packaged, if so numbered. Cut tiles neatly around all fixtures. Discard broken, cracked, chipped, or deformed tiles.

> RETAIN 1 REQUIREMENT FROM 3 SUBPARAGRAPHS BELOW OR INSERT ANOTHER.

Lay tiles with grain running in one direction.

Lay tiles in basket weave pattern with grain direction alternating between reversed in adjacent tiles.

Lay tiles in pattern with respect to location of colors, patterns, and sizes as indicated on Drawings.

Where demountable partitions and other items are indicated for installing on top of finished tile floor, install tile before these items are installed.

> CORRELATE ABOVE WITH ITEMS DESCRIBED BELOW. IF ANY BUILT-IN ITEMS ARE SET ON TOP OF TILE, INDICATE ACCORDINGLY ON DRAWINGS.

Scribe, cut, and fit tiles to butt tightly to vertical surfaces, permanent fixtures, built-in furniture including cabinets, pipes, outlets, edgings, thresholds, and nosings.

Extend tiles into toe spaces, door reveals, closets, and similar openings.

Maintain reference markers, holes, or openings that are in place or plainly marked for future cutting by repeating on finish flooring as marked on subfloor. Use chalk or other nonpermanent marking device.

> DELETE BELOW IF NO COVERS.

Install tiles on covers for telephone and electrical ducts, and similar items occurring within finished floor areas. Maintain overall continuity of color and pattern with pieces of flooring installed on these covers. Tightly adhere edges to perimeter of floor around covers and to covers.

Adhere tiles to flooring substrates without producing open cracks, voids, raising and puckering at joints, telegraphing of adhesive spreader marks, or other surface imperfections in completed tile installation.

> REVISE BELOW IF OTHER THAN FULL SPREAD METHOD USED AND RECOMMENDED BY TILE MFR FOR SUBSTRATE AND TILE PRODUCT INDICATED.

Use full spread of adhesive applied to substrate in compliance with tile manufacturer's directions including those for trowel notching, adhesive mixing, and adhesive open and working times.

> DELETE BELOW IF ROLLING NOT REQUIRED BY TILE MFRS SPECIFIED.

Hand roll tiles where required by tile manufacturer.

CLEANING AND PROTECTION

Perform the following operations immediately after completing tile installation:

RESILIENT TILE FLOORING   09660 - 6

FINISH SCHEDULE

NO.	ROOM NAME	FLOOR					BASE			WALLS — NORTH					WALLS — EAST					WALLS — WEST					WALLS — SOUTH					CEILING		HGT.	REMARKS
		CARPET 1	CARPET 2	CARPET 3	VCT	WOOD	OAK	RUBBER 1	RUBBER 2	WALLCOVERING 1	WALLCOVERING 2	PAINT 1	PAINT 2	UNFINISHED	WALLCOVERING 1	WALLCOVERING 2	PAINT 1	PAINT 2	UNFINISHED	WALLCOVERING 1	WALLCOVERING 2	PAINT 1	PAINT 2	UNFINISHED	WALLCOVERING 1	WALLCOVERING 2	PAINT 1	PAINT 2	UNFINISHED	CEILING 1	CEILING 2		
101	RECEPTION AREA	●		●			●			●	●				●	●				●	●				●	●							
102	OFFICE	●					●			●		●			●		●			●		●			●		●						
103	OFFICE	●					●			●		●			●		●			●		●			●		●						
104	SUPPLY ROOM				●				●						●			●					●							●				
105	SECRETARY		●					●		●	●				●	●				●	●				●	●							
106	CORRIDOR		●					●			●	●				●	●				●	●				●	●						
107	OFFICE	●					●			●		●			●		●			●		●			●		●						
108	EXECUTIVE OFFICE	●		●			●			●	●				●	●				●	●				●	●							
109	OFFICE	●					●			●		●			●		●			●		●			●		●						
110	WORK ROOM				●			●						●			●					●							●				
111	OFFICE	●					●			●		●			●		●			●		●			●		●						
112	FILE ROOM				●			●						●			●					●							●				
113	OFFICE	●					●			●		●			●		●			●		●			●		●						
114	CORRIDOR		●					●			●	●				●	●				●	●				●	●						
115	OFFICE	●					●			●		●			●		●			●		●			●		●						
116	SECRETARY		●					●		●	●				●	●				●	●				●	●							
117	SECRETARY		●					●		●	●				●	●				●	●				●	●							
118	OFFICE	●					●			●		●			●		●			●		●			●		●						
119	OFFICE	●					●			●		●			●		●			●		●			●		●						
120	BREAK ROOM				●				●						●			●					●							●				

FLOOR

CARPET 1	BENTLEY KING'S ROAD ROSE #243
CARPET 2	BENTLEY KING'S ROAD BEIGE #256
CARPET 3	BENTLEY KING'S ROAD MAUVE #226
VCT	ARMSTRONG EXCELON GRAY #25
WOOD	OAK PARQUET, 6 × 6 INCHES

BASE

OAK	BENTLEY KING'S ROAD ROSE #243
RUBBER 1	ROPPE #26 GRAY
RUBBER 2	ROPPE #18 WHITE

WALLS

WALLCOVERING 1	GENON STIPPLE STRIPE GRAY #243-8
WALLCOVERING 2	GENON PEBBLE ROSE #167-5
PAINT 1	SHERWIN WILLIAMS TRULY TEAL SW-1476
PAINT 2	SHERWIN WILLIAMS SILVERSCREEN SW-1015

CEILING

CEILING 1	ARMSTRONG SECOND LOOK II WHITE
CEILING 2	ARMSTRONG NUBBY WHITE

A CHART-STYLE FINISH SCHEDULE THAT USES BULLETS TO INDICATE WHICH FINISHES ARE USED IN THE ROOMS OF ONE LARGE FLOOR OF AN OFFICE BUILDING.

PROFESSIONAL ORGANIZATIONS

Given the wide range of materials and finishes discussed in this book, it is assumed that the reader will require sources for further information. While an exhaustive list of finish and materials manufacturers would be a valuable resource, it would be nearly impossible to compile. The professional organizations listed below can provide interested interior designers and architects with up-to-date information concerning each finish and discipline, and are best able to refer designers to an appropriate alternative source if necessary.

GENERAL

American Institute of Architects
1735 New York Avenue, N.W.
Washington, D.C. 20006
(202) 626-7300

American Society of Interior Designers
608 Massachusetts Avenue, N.E.
Washington, D.C. 20002
(202) 546-3480

Institute of Business Designers
341 Merchandise Mart
Chicago, Illinois 60654
(312) 467-1950

CONSTRUCTION MATERIALS AND BUILDING

American Concrete Institute
P.O. Box 19150
Detroit, Michigan 48219
(313) 532-2600

Gypsum Association
810 1st Street, N.E., #510
Washington, D.C. 20002
(202) 289-5440

WOOD AND WOOD PRODUCTS

American Plywood Association
P.O. Box 11700
Tacoma, Washington 98411
(206) 565-6600

Wood Moulding & Millwork Producers Association
P.O. Box 25278
Portland, Oregon 97225
(503) 292-9288

Wood Flooring Association
11046 Manchester Road
St. Louis, Missouri 63122
(314) 821-8654

STONE

Marble Institute of America
33505 State Street
Farmington, Michigan 48335
(313) 476-5558

BRICK AND MASONRY

Masonry Institute of America
823 15th Street, N.W.
Washington, D.C. 20005
(202) 783-3908

METALS

American Society of Metals
9639 Kinsman
Materials Park, Ohio 44073
(216) 338-5151

CERAMIC AND QUARRY TILE

Ceramic Tile Institute of America
700 North Virgil Avenue
Los Angeles, California 90029
(213) 660-1911

Tile Council of America
P.O. Box 326
Princeton, New Jersey 08542
(609) 921-7050

RESILIENT FLOORING

Resilient Floor Covering Institute
966 Hungerford Drive
Suite 12B
Rockville, Maryland 20805
(301) 340-8580

CARPETING

Carpet and Rug Institute
P.O. Box 2048
Dalton, Georgia 30722
(404) 278-3176

PAINT

National Paint and Coatings
Association
1500 Rhode Island Avenue, N.W.
Washington, D.C. 20005
(202) 462-6272

WALLCOVERINGS

Wallcovering Information Bureau
355 Lexington Avenue
17th floor
New York, New York 10017
(212) 661-4261

CEILING MATERIALS

Ceiling and Interior Systems
Construction Associates
104 Wilmot Road
Suite 201
Deerfield, Illinois 60015
(708) 940-8800

FURNITURE

Furniture Manufacturers
Association
220 Lyon Street, N.W.
Box HP-7
Highpoint, North Carolina 27261
(919) 884-5000

CASEWORK AND TRIM

Architectural Woodwork Institute
2310 South Walter Reed Drive
Arlington, Virginia 22206
(703) 671-9100

FINISHES EVALUATION, SPECIFICATION, AND SCHEDULING

Masterspec
Construction Specifications
Institute
601 Madison Street
Alexandria, Virginia 22314
(703) 684-0300

INDEX